may be

ENVIRONMENTS IN PROFILE

Environments in Profile

AN AQUATIC PERSPECTIVE

W. MICHAEL KAILL
University of the Pacific, Stockton, Ca.

JOHN K. FREY
Franklin High School, Stockton, Ca.

CANFIELD PRESS   San Francisco
A Department of Harper & Row, Publishers, Inc.
New York   Evanston   London

ENVIRONMENTS IN PROFILE

An Aquatic Perspective

Copyright © 1973 by W. Michael Kaill and John K. Frey
Printed in the United States of America. All rights
reserved. No part of this book may be used or
reproduced in any manner whatsoever without written
permission except in the case of brief quotations
embodied in critical articles and reviews.
For information address Harper & Row, Publishers, Inc.,
10 East 53rd Street, New York, N.Y. 10022.

International Standard Book Number: 0-06-384465-6
Library of Congress Catalog Card Number: 73-1027

73 74 75 10 9 8 7 6 5 4 3 2

Cover photograph by Ernest Braun

*Epigraph from TAO TEH KING by Lao Tzu, translated
by Archie J. Bahm. Copyright © 1958 by Frederick
Ungar Publishing Co., Inc. Reprinted by permission.*

Nature sustains itself through three precious principles,
which one does well to embrace and follow.
These are gentleness, frugality and humility.
When one is gentle, he has no fear of retaliation.
When one is frugal, he can afford to be generous.
When one is humble, no one challenges his leadership.
But when rudeness replaces gentleness,
And extravagance replaces frugality,
And pride replaces humility,
Then one is doomed.
Since a gentle attack arouses little antagonism,
And a gentle defense provokes little anger,
Nature predisposes to gentleness those most suited for
survival.

Lao Tzu, TAO TEH KING

Contents

Preface

The best way to learn basic principles of ecology is through direct observation of those principles. *Environments in Profile* facilitates such observation. Keys, field, and laboratory techniques are provided for evaluation of environmental conditions. There is a materials section, so that this analysis can be conducted as easily and efficiently as possible. An introductory theoretical section is provided to assure that field procedures make sense, and also to assure that increasing experience in field work results in increasing development of ecological perspective. The "environmental profile" takes things a step further. It allows the student to plot his data graphically and to visualize the relationships there. He can determine the way in which environmental factors affect one another and the way in which environments change with time (such as daily or seasonal changes).

In other words, we have tried to bring together three approaches:

those of classroom, field trip, and textbook. From this background the student should be able to reinforce the perspective gained by visualizing the significance of relationships which he himself has recorded. Through this combination we hope that the information gap which exists between the journalistic level of environmental information and the level of professional biology and chemistry will be filled.

Although the physico-chemical and ecological processes are complex, the basic principles involved are not. Thanks to advances in both chemistry and packaging, new techniques for environmental testing are available. These techniques allow testing without the technological training and laboratory facilities that were necessary in the past.

A variety of tests and techniques are presented in which a student can understand what is going on and can determine for himself the nature of the environment in question. Some of the tests presented are acceptable as public health water quality monitoring techniques. Using such techniques, students already have become active in civic efforts to improve local environmental conditions. Wherever possible, several alternatives for a determination are presented so that persons with tight budgets can select an appropriate technique.

The aquatic environment is ideal for learning basic ecological principles. Even in a course emphasizing terrestrial ecology, the concepts of succession, energy and nutrient flow, trophic levels, limiting factors, and others can all be observed easily in an aquatic system. These phenomena may be demonstrated in nothing more than a small aquarium. Microscopic aquatic organisms are essentially the same for any given type of freshwater environment. Also, with few exceptions, dominant aquatic plants and animals are the same throughout the United States, primarily through introductions into similar habitats. In most cases this means that a key or biological lab can be used virtually anywhere in the United States. Because of local influences and local faunas, terrestrial environments are precluded from such a universal approach. Nonetheless, some terrestrial procedures are included here, since the effect of the surrounding land on the aquatic environment cannot be ignored.

In field work, one is not able to predict examples, or what will be encountered first; therefore, this book is designed so that any part can be used independently of the other parts. It is compatible with either a traditional or a relatively unstructured approach. It can serve as a text, guide, or handbook. The approach to field investigation described here can be integrated with courses in principles of biology, environmental biology, field biology, or man and the environment. The same field approach is valuable in more specialized courses in ecology or aquatic biology.

Our approach is a positive one. Whenever possible, we have tried to avoid saying in effect: "Memorize this. It is valuable, and you will understand why later." In a first course in ecology, aquatic biology, or principles of biology, a student has a good deal of curiosity and positive feeling for what is happening around him. If he can operate under his own motivation, he has a more meaningful learning experience. Thus, the flexibility of *Environments in Profile* allows it to be used at an individual level as well as in class activities.

This book is organized into three parts. The first part is concerned with principles. Too often, students ask, "Why do we need to determine oxygen? What does 8 ppm mean?" Part I provides answers to these questions. From this part the student should gain both an understanding of and an appreciation for the interrelatedness of a natural system.

The second part is the "how to" section. The principles of Part I are put to work in field and laboratory measurements. Each of these environmental tests measures a small fraction of the ecosystem under study. The student needs to perceive the unity of the ecosystem by considering all of the environmental conditions simultaneously. The environmental profile is one way in which this unification can be accomplished. Only when the parts are consolidated can one appreciate the entire ecosystem. Multiple copies of the blank profile chart (inside back cover) should be used to organize the data from field observations.

The appendix supplies practical information. Suggestions are included on field trip planning, caring for equipment, and organization of field data. It also lists suppliers, materials, directions for preparation of solutions, and, where possible, directions for construction of equipment. References for more technical works and related topics are also included in this section.

Environments in Profile has a clear purpose. It is not another ecology textbook, nor is it an attempt to duplicate the impressive keys and guides to freshwater biology already available. It is a simple, nonmathematical, concise means of putting together the many approaches that compose the discipline of ecology.

Stockton, California   W.M.K.
February 1973   J.K.F.

Acknowledgments

We would like to thank the following people: Lorna Cunkle, Steven Hoffman, Robert Kano, and Robert Loken. Our thanks also are extended to professors William Gladfelter, Pacific Marine Station; Robert A. Main, California State University, Hayward; and Dale McNeal, University of the Pacific for their comments and suggestions. We are particularly indebted to Roger Gymer, California State University, Fresno; Diane Hersh; Alan Holbert, Cabrillo College; Peter Moyle, University of California, Davis; Robert L. Smith, West Virginia University; Carlo Vecchiarelli, Chabot College; and Stephen Wolfe, University of California, Davis,—all of whom were especially helpful in the preparation of this book. Our original ideas for this project were developed as part of an In-service Institute sponsored by the National Science Foundation, Grant number G-W 5713. We would also like to thank the staff of Canfield Press: Pat Brewer, Lisa Goldberg, Julie Kranhold, and our editor Wayne Oler. Key art was drawn by Thelma Norian. A special thanks to our wives, Annie and Chris, for their patience and understanding through this project.

CONCEPTUAL
BACKGROUND

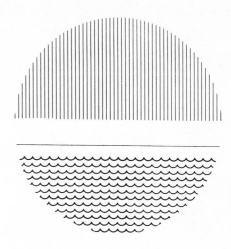

In many ways, water is the best place to study ecology. The aquatic environment is commonly a very intense living system. Unlike the terrestrial system, water offers physical support with nutrients suspended in the environment. Because of its density, temperature characteristics, and other properties, the water environment tends to be more stable than the land (Reid, 1961). One can study and observe population phenomena and ecological principles in a small pond that would take acres of land to duplicate. A microcosm, a miniature version of larger systems, can be observed in a water sample. The reaction of the biological community to contaminants can be seen much more swiftly in an aquatic environment than in similar terrestrial situations. Water carries wastes away. Although it is said that water purifies itself, material dumped into water does not simply disappear. It becomes a part of the aquatic system. Many principles of ecology are available for study from the introduction of these materials through the process of their purification.

The aquatic and terrestrial worlds are different, but they are not separated. Water flows over and through the earth and, as the earth is dissolved, it becomes part of the water. Water soaks into the earth and is taken up by plants and animals to become part of the terrestrial system. Water evaporates and becomes part of the air. Then it condenses as snow or rain and may become part of a lake or a river, or it may slowly percolate through the earth to finally reach the ocean.

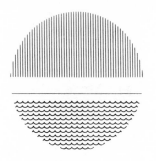

1. Principles of Ecology

Ecosystems

An ecosystem is the total of all the relationships of the living and nonliving parts of an environment. The term ecosystem reflects the total relatedness of nature. There is no line separating living and nonliving, water and air. Water, minerals, and energy-supplying materials are in constant circulation. All of these things flow in and out of animal bodies, plant bodies, lakes, and streams.

Many movements of materials are regular enough to be called cycles. For example, the circular movement of water from the sea by evaporation, to the land by precipitation, and through the ground to the sea again is called the hydrological cycle (Figure 1–1). However, most cycles are not as regular and consistent as the hydrological cycle.

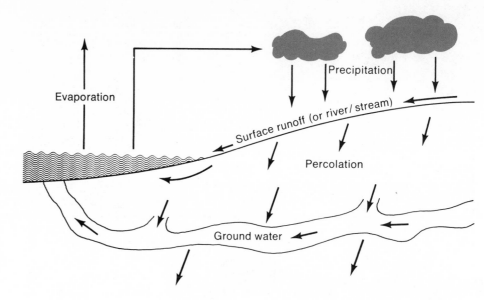

Figure 1–1   A Hydrological Cycle. Note evaporation of water from the ocean, cloud movement to land mass, precipitation, and movement through land mass to return to the sea.

Nutrient Cycles

Another example of a natural cycle is the movement of certain nutrients (chemical building materials, such as compounds of phosphorus, nitrogen, and sulfur). To appreciate the importance of nutrients, it is convenient to visualize a checklist of conditions necessary to support a complete community. A community is the interrelated total of plant and animal populations in an area, while a population is all the individuals of one species within that area. Supplies of light, water, carbon, and the nutrient building materials are necessary. If one of the items on the list is missing, the whole interrelated system fails. The community cannot exist unless it has all of its requirements. Every species within a community requires particular conditions for its survival. If one of these conditions is absent, the species will die or growth and development will be restricted. If one of these requirements is present in small amounts, the population size of the species will be limited. The "law of the minimum" states that the size of the population is controlled by the requirement that occurs in minimal amounts. For example, if phosphate is scarce, the community will grow until it has used up the phosphate. Further growth will be minimal. Ecologists term this situation a phosphate-limited system, obeying the "law of the minimum."

Plant growth takes place in the lighted, upper regions of the water. Nutrient materials tend to settle down into the unlighted, deep waters where there is no plant growth. Under these conditions, the important building materials (nutrients) end up separated from the only place where plants can grow. The nutrient cycle seems to be incomplete (Figure 1–2). But the phosphate is not really gone; it is trapped in the mud and deeper waters. The plants in the upper, warmer, sunlit waters ("floating" over the cooler, lower waters), do not have this nutrient. During much of the growing season, the temperature difference between upper and lower waters contributes to the establishment of a thermocline (Chap. 2), which restricts circulation between upper and deeper waters and maintains differences in phosphate concentration. Since phosphate is required for the life processes of these plants, its absence becomes limiting and plant populations are reduced, obeying the "law of the minimum" (Figure 1–2).

This nutrient cycle explains the green water "spring blooms" (temporary rich growth in lakes). During the early part of the stable growing season, there are abundant nutrients in the surface waters. The plants grow rapidly, then something, usually nitrogen or phosphorus compounds, becomes scarce (or "limiting" because its absence limits

Figure 1-2 *Nutrient Cycle: phosphate cycle in lake with thermocline. Phosphate occurs in living organisms of lighted zone. As plants and animals die, they sink out of the lighted zone, past the compensation depth into the unlighted zone. The compensation depth is the depth in which light intensity is just strong enough for the plants to photosynthesize the energy that they need to stay alive. The phosphate in the unlighted zone is often prevented from returning to the lighted zone by a barrier to circulation, the thermocline. Phosphate-rich materials get incorporated into bottom muds, also out of the circulation pattern. Phosphate (and thus plants and animals) becomes scarce in the lighted zone, which may remain sterile until the deeper, nutrient-rich water is circulated when the thermocline barrier breaks down. When such circulation occurs, a "bloom" usually results. The dotted arrow represents such circulation.*

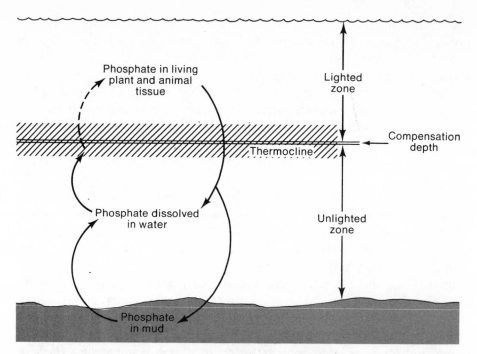

the size of the population). The vigor and development of individuals within the population is also affected. The plants die and the water subsequently clears up. It usually stays clear through the summer. The cooling temperature and fall winds circulate the water, and cause upwelling, which brings the nutrients back from the bottom. The checklist is complete again, and a "fall bloom" is produced.

Energy Flow

Even though there may be traps (e.g., mud) in nutrient cycles, they are all basically circular. Energy transfer, in contrast, is not circular.

The energy entering our atmosphere (all energy on the earth is originally derived from the sun) is transferred through a series of steps: sun, to plant (through the process of photosynthesis), to herbivore (plant eater), to carnivore (meat eater). Each step of energy transfer is called a trophic level (Figure 1–3). At each trophic level the remaining amount of original energy is decreased. Of a hundred units of sun's energy, only 1 unit of that energy may actually become plant tissue. (The unit value used here is arbitrary.) The other 99 units are lost in the form of heat, reflected light, and energy demands of the plants. When a plant is eaten, only a fraction (0.1) of the one unit retained by the plant may actually be used to make the herbivore's body tissue. The other 0.9 units are converted to body heat and other forms of "lost" energy.

Because of the decrease in available energy at each trophic level, there will normally be fewer living things at each step. This is one explanation for the fact that there are more herbivores than carnivores. And there are more carnivores that eat herbivores than carnivores that eat other carnivores. If an organism can omit intermediate steps and go directly to the plants, it will have more usable energy available to it.

Trophic
levels

Sunlight 100 units of original energy (not to scale)

Plants (phytoplankton in surface water) = 1.0 unit of energy remaining

one

Herbivores (zooplankton) = 0.1 unit of energy remaining

two

Carnivores (fish) = 0.01 unit of energy remaining

three

Figure 1–3 Trophic levels. All of the energy entering the system is from sunlight. Of 100 energy units of available sunlight, in a hypothetical system, 1.0 unit is converted into plants in the first trophic level. The remaining 99 units of energy is "lost" as heat and unused light. The animals feeding on the plants then retain 0.1 unit of the available plant energy, and so on. (Shaded areas not to scale.)

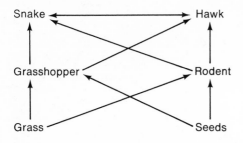

Figure 1-4 Two food chains are indicated by the vertical arrows. The direction of the arrows indicates direction of food energy. The food web is indicated by the diagonal arrows forming connections between the two chains. Note the increased food opportunities for an animal in a food web as compared to the opportunities for that animal in a food chain.

Often in nations of high population density, such as China, the people cannot afford the energy lost by existing at a third trophic level. Their diets, low in meat and high in plants (rice), are mostly on a second trophic level position. This allows them to use the increased energy available at that level (Figure 1-3).

The plant to herbivore to carnivore series is called a food chain (Figure 1-4). There may be several food chains in a community, such as grass to grasshopper to snake or seed to rodent to hawk. When the carnivore (hawk) from one food chain feeds on an organism (snake) from another chain, the food chains become interconnected and form a "food web." Because a carnivore has alternative food sources in a food web, the web is a more stable community situation. As a rule, the more complex the food web, the more stable the community, because animals at each step of the food chain have alternative sources of energy. It must be realized that some of the energy of a food web ends up in the form of waste products and dead plant and animal material. This organic material supports the decomposer community.

Eutrophication

A lake, after decades of slow filling, becomes a shallow, overgrown marsh and, through continued filling, a meadow. This aging process involves some filling by inert materials such as sand, rock, and gravel. More substantial contributions often result from eutrophication. Eutrophication is the increase of nutrients (particularly those likely to be limiting, such as compounds of phosphorus and nitrogen) as well as the effects of such a nutrient increase. The added nutrients encourage plant growth. Plants increase in abundance and so do animals supported by the plant populations. Increased amounts of dead plants settle to the bottom and gradually reduce the lake depth, hastening the filling process. The result is a eutrophic or "well-nourished" lake, with large amounts of algae and other sources of organic material. In contrast, an oligotrophic lake is nutrient poor, with low populations of plants and animals (oligotrophic lakes are often "young"). A mesotrophic lake is midway between the rich eutrophic condition, and the essentially sterile oligotrophic state.

Excessive organic input due to man's activities is called cultural eutrophication. Some of the contributions to cultural eutrophication are artificial fertilizers (of crops, golf courses, and even of household gardens and lawns) that eventually find their way into river systems. Detergents contribute phosphates (without the detergent, low phosphate levels might be a limiting factor). Road construction, if not properly done, causes erosion and can add soil nutrients to the water.

The lines of demarcation separating lake classifications are not clear. The ends of the spectrum can easily be labeled; but labeling the intermediate stages that range from oligotrophic to eutrophic is a subjective judgment, based on information like that assembled in the environmental profile (Chap. 14).

Tolerance Limits

When conditions in a lake or stream deteriorate, we think of many of the species populations in the water as "dying off." But this is rarely the case. Any species has evolved through millions of years to survive most efficiently within a certain range of environmental conditions. For example, a species' temperature range has a central optimum, and a high and low which represent the tolerance limits of the species. Research in recent years has demonstrated that temperature extremes are not usually the direct cause of population die-off. In a natural situation, the population under stress will be eliminated by competition before the temperature has reached a tolerance limit.

As an organism's environment approaches the tolerance limit, it is also moving away from the optimum levels. For example, a fish has an optimum of 70°F with upper and lower tolerances of 85°F and 55°F. When the water is warmer than 70°, the fish is no longer at optimum. The closer the temperature gets to a tolerance limit, the more stress is placed on the animal. Heat can be considered a pollutant because it places a stress upon the animal and weakens it, reducing its ability to compete with other species. Stress caused by an environmental condition that is near tolerance level is a form of sublethal pollution.

Rainbow trout have a temperature optimum around 60°F. They can be kept in artificial ponds at temperatures up to 70°–75°F if no other species are present. At the higher temperatures they are less efficient at food utilization, less responsive, and their appetite is not as sharp. If those same trout are in a natural stream or lake at those temperatures, the stress induced by the high temperature causes a reduced efficiency of operation compared to efficiency at 60°F. Other fishes, with optimum levels nearer the environmental temperature, out-compete the trout.

Upper and lower tolerance levels exist for salinity, dissolved oxygen, carbon dioxide, and many other factors just as they do for temperature.

Niche

If all of the tolerance limits are superimposed upon one another, e.g., 50°–70°F temperature, 5 to 8 parts per million (ppm) of oxygen, 0 to 5 parts per thousand (o/oo) of salinity, a system of tolerance ranges becomes apparent. The animal must remain between 50°F and 70°F, the water cannot be too salty, and so forth. Such tolerance ranges are a part of the description of an organism's niche, which is defined as the totality of its requirements. For example, tolerance ranges describe physical conditions, and food requirements describe trophic level. One interesting way of visualizing an organism's niche is to consider the ranges of conditions under which the organism can live (Hutchinson, 1965). The space thus described (a "hyperspace") encloses the niche. Optimal conditions are near the center, marginal conditions are near the edges. As competition with other organisms occurs, the ranges of conditions that the species can tolerate are reduced (the hyperspace shrinks in the region of competition). As extremes in one condition are encountered (as the animal is forced near an edge of its niche hyperspace), the ranges of many other conditions which the animal can tolerate are reduced. A niche is the end result of the interactions of a species and its physical and biological environment, through evolutionary time.

The adaptations of plants and animals that allow them to cope with environmental conditions are coded in complex genetic material. Therefore, any sexually reproducing population is not one "type" but a series of variations. No two such organisms are just alike.

Each generation produces a new group of organisms, some of which will not survive to mate and contribute to the next generation. Often the reasons for survival or nonsurvival are indirect. For example, physiological adaptations that allow animals to cope with temperature or adjust rapidly to new temperatures, reduce stress on the organism. The reduced stress saves energy that can be put to some other use (such as food-getting). The holder of such an adaptation has an advantage. Often, adaptations are advantageous to an organism in a particular restricted region. Through natural selection, color, size, and shape of plants and animals are likely to be influenced by local conditions (e.g., coat colors of small mammals match the color of local soils). When plants and animals are adapted in such a way to local conditions, they are termed ecotypes.

As conditions within an environment change, the environment will favor those animals that are adapted to the new conditions. Such a statement holds not only for the *levels* of conditions (e.g., for heat or cold), but it also holds for the amount of *variation* in conditions that an animal can stand (e.g., the temperature extremes of one day or one season). A trout may have an optimum temperature of 60°F and tolerance limits at 50°F and 70°F. At the same time, a carp may have a tolerance range of 35°F to 100°F. Each species has evolved in response to a particular habitat.

> The habitat of an organism is the place where it lives, or the place where one would go to find it. The *ecological niche,* on the other hand, is a more inclusive term that includes not only the physical space occupied by an organism, but also its functional role in the community (as, for example, its trophic position) and its position in environmental gradients of temperature, moisture, pH, soil, and other conditions of existence (Odum, 1971: 234).

The trout's habitat is rather constant, and as a result, the trout has become specialized to the conditions of a trout stream. The trout, through evolutionary time, has become efficient at living in his particular environment with its narrow range of conditions. The carp, on the other hand, has evolved in an environment of widely variable conditions. The carp is well adapted to the inconstant (often implying polluted) habitat. It and others having similar wide tolerances are often included as part of the "pollution community."

The trout can be considered a specialist, adapted for existence in a single type of environment. The carp, then, is the generalist, adapted for existence in many kinds of environments. The carp does well, unless he has to compete with a specialist on the specialist's own ground. The trout might be compared to a technician, and the carp to a jack-of-all-trades. As long as the situation is stable and there are constant niches available, the technicians (trout) will do fine. But instability or a lack of the constant, narrow, specialist, niche situation will favor the jack-of-all-trades or the carp (MacArthur and Connell, 1967).

While some ecologists will argue the point, there generally appears to be a correlation between the numbers of specialists, stability, and what man values as a high-quality environment. In a stable situation the specialists have divided up the available positions. In ecological terms, they have a narrow niche division. With such narrow ranges of habitat use, there is room for many different specialties, although there may not be many individuals in each of the specialties. In ecological terms, we can say that there is species diversity.

In a polluted or unstable situation, the specialist does not succeed. The generalist (jack-of-all-trades) takes over. It has a wide range of tolerances, or a wide niche division. A community in an unstable habitat may be small, measured by number of species, and large measured by numbers of each species (Figure 1–5).

Population Regulation

The kinds and numbers of animals present may tell a lot about an environment before the water quality has been chemically measured. Figure 1–5 summarizes the relationships between numbers of individuals

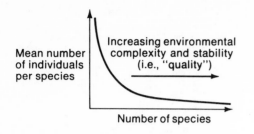

Figure 1–5 Relationship between species diversity, numbers of each species, and environmental "quality." As the number of species (horizontal scale) increases, the mean number of individuals per species (vertical scale) decreases, that is, more different kinds of animals are seen. Comparing extremes, the fish population of a tropical reef would be on the far right of the scale, showing many different kinds of species, with just a few individuals of each species in any local area. The salt marsh fish populations would be on the left hand side of the scale, composed of large populations of a few species. This reflects the relatively unstable conditions brought about by the shallow water and tides (see Odum, 1971: 149).

in a species, numbers of species, and "quality" (environmental complexity and stability) of the environment. If the relationship is put in mathematical form, habitats can be assessed on the basis of presence or absence of generalists and specialists using the Diversity Index (Chap. 14).

One of the problems that any population faces is that of maintaining a reasonable population size, in terms of the amount of resources available. This problem also faces the human population. Under optimum conditions, populations tend to increase rapidly. Consider the following hypothetical example in which every generation doubles the population size. If a pair of organisms produce 4 offspring, then each pair of the next generation produce 4 offspring, the population increase with each *successive generation* is 2, 4, 8, 16, 32, 64, 128, 256, 512, 1024, 2048, 4096, etc. If such a population increase is plotted as in Figure 1–6, it produces a growth rate curve (Kormundy, 1969: 64).

The problem with such a growth rate is that once the initial stages are past, the increase is extremely rapid and difficult to control. Further, any habitat has a limit to the number of plants and animals that it can support. As a population grows, it draws on the resources of the environment at a rate that is proportional to its size. Sooner or later the population encounters a limitation in the food or nutrient supply, or the supply of oxygen, or even the ability of the environment to assimilate waste products. The size of the population (numbers of individuals) at the time that the limiting factor becomes effective is called the carrying capacity. If the carrying capacity is reached on the left part of the curve (Figure 1–6), where there are not many individuals and where the rate of growth is still slow, the population may be able to stabilize. But if the population growth reaches a carrying capacity located somewhere on the steep slope on the right portion of the curve, it is difficult to stabilize population size. An environment has resources (e.g., grass for cattle) to support only a certain number (carrying capacity) of animals. If the carrying

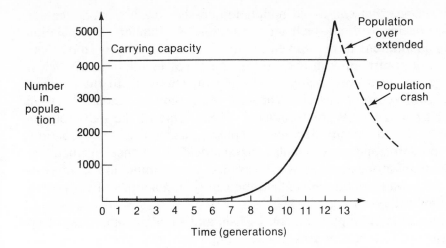

Figure 1–6 *Hypothetical growth rate curve showing population size exceeding carrying capacity with resultant die-off (crash) of population.*

capacity is exceeded, the environment is altered (e.g., grass is consumed to the ground by the cattle when the land is over-grazed). The environment is damaged, and the carrying capacity is reduced.

Many young organisms, simply by growing into adults, increase the demand on the environment. This and other kinds of population inertia tend to project the population beyond carrying capacity once it gets on the high rise part of the growth curve. Under these conditions it is easy for such a population to exceed the carrying capacity. A population exceeding carrying capacity is living on borrowed time, and soon runs out of some needed resource. With the needed resource scarce and natural reserves gone, few animals get proper amounts of the resource and few are healthy. There is a "crash" with death, parasitism, and disease widespread. The population shrinks to a fraction of its former size, and sometimes dies out altogether.

A species that can avoid population crashes has a great advantage over a species without such an adaptation. A number of population control adaptations have evolved in various animals. This is an interesting area of controversy in ecology: animals that maintain levels below carrying capacity pose many interesting questions as to their means of "sensing" current carrying capacity levels and of regulating group size (Hazen, 1970; Wynne-Edwards, 1962). One of the most reliable of the so-called density-dependent control mechanisms is predation. Many predator and prey populations are held in balance by their dependency upon one another. An illustration can be found in the interesting series of studies on wolves and their prey populations of caribou or deer (Pimlott, 1967).

Large kills of amphibians, birds, fish, and small mammals can often be attributed to levels of growth exceeding carrying capacity. Fish kills are sometimes the results of algal blooms. Planktonic plants and animals (free-floating microscopic organisms) may exceed the environmental supplies of oxygen during the night (plants require oxygen when not photosynthesizing). The oxygen concentration then drops to levels that suffocate the fish, killing them in large numbers. Other causes of oxygen depletion are metabolic oxygen demands of the decomposer population, working on dead materials from algal blooms. Such kills can sometimes be traced to "nutrient pollution," unusually large amounts of nutrient materials that remove the limits from the plankton populations and increase them beyond the population size typical of the habitat. When the plankton reach or exceed carrying capacity, the environment (including oxygen concentration) may be altered.

Succession

Community stability is often dependent upon a system of checks and balances. An established community has developed within a framework of certain conditions. If the conditions are altered (e.g., by extensive predator control or by unusually large amounts of nutrient materials), the system must readjust to the new conditions. Often it is permanently altered.

The natural development of a complex and stable community structure comes through a series of stages. Each stage increases the complexity of the community. This process of increasing the stability and complexity of an environment is called ecological succession. The early forms in a succession are often called the pioneer communities. The final stage, at which no more changes occur with additional time, is called the climax community. A typical terrestrial succession is grass—shrub—pine—oak—beech (Figure 1–7).

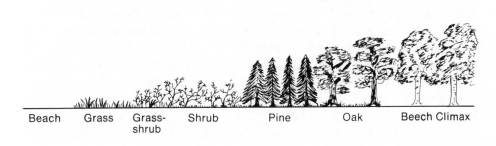

Beach   Grass   Grass-shrub   Shrub   Pine   Oak   Beech Climax

Figure 1–7 Composite succession scheme. The bare field is first populated by the pioneer grasses and weeds. The habitat is then suitably stabilized for the growth of shrubs. With abundant shrub population, pines are able to find suitable habitat, and a pine forest produces an even more stable and complex community, which allows the oak and other deciduous species to establish populations. The succession if stopped at any point, for various reasons (soil type, fire, human modification, etc.), is termed disclimax.

A cleared and plowed field represents an unstable physical situation. When it is sunny, the soil is dried; and when it rains, the soil is directly pelted by the drops. Temperature and humidity as well as many other factors vary widely from day to day, and often from hour to hour. Such an environment is not favorable for most organisms. Life under such conditions would have to tolerate wide ranges of many environmental conditions.

The grasses as well as many weeds (ragweed and smartweed) are wide-tolerance plants (pioneer species), and are usually the first plants to be seen in a bare environment, such as a plowed field or a beach. They are adapted for the wide range of conditions to be met in such a situation, and are able to establish a population. Once the grasses or weeds are established, the conditions are not as variable as they were before. The presence of the pioneer species provides some stability. The humidity is more constant, the substrate is held from shifting by the roots of the plants, and there is often the beginning of a humus or organic litter provided by the dead leaves and other parts of the plants.

Another group of plants, represented by the shrubs, does not have the tolerance abilities shown by the grasses and weeds. But once environmental fluctuations are narrowed by the pioneer species, the shrubs are able to make an appearance and survive. The shrubs' presence adds even more stability, and soon the grasses (with pioneer adaptations) are in competition for a habitat that is no longer at the pioneer stage. The shrubs, thriving under the conditions of partial stability provided by the pioneer species, out-compete them. The shrubs continue the development of stability, and allow young pine trees to become established.

In certain cases, succession is held at one of the intermediate points. On a beach where conditions of water action and wind do not permit stability beyond the pioneer grass stage, there is no succession beyond the dune grass environment. Working inland from a beach, the steps in a succession series can be observed (Figure 1–7). A similar situation is found in the pine-palmetto regions of the southeastern United States. Succession in these regions would normally proceed to a pine forest stage and finally to a forest of deciduous trees. But in this part of the country, there are frequent fires which burn off the shrubs and only char the fire-resistant pines. Under the influence of periodic fires, succession to a "natural" climax is halted. Instead, a permanent intermediate stage or "disclimax" is seen.

The fire ecology disclimax situation is interesting in light of efforts of The National Forest Service to stop forest fires. Fires are less frequent, with two common results. First, the litter from the trees and palmetto piles up so that when a fire does occur it is very hot and kills the normally protected roots of the shrubs, the pines, and the animals deep in their burrows. All of these can survive in the normally less hot but more frequent fire situation. Second, the succession continues with young trees and large shrubs crowding the former open understory. As a result the animal population changes from the quail and other game species that the citizens of the region prize so highly. In an effort to solve problems posed by an unwanted succession from disclimax, many forestry agencies are practicing programs of experimental burning.

In aquatic situations, the pioneer species are represented by the bacteria (note the slick scum on the sides of a glass of water left out for several days). Small protozoans and algae are usually the next stage. They give way to large protozoans, then to more complex forms such as hydroids and large-branched algae. The whole process is rapid and can be demonstrated in a large, water-filled, glass jar. Only a few weeks are required to complete the process of succession if some hay or grass is added to provide a starter.

2. Important Environmental Factors

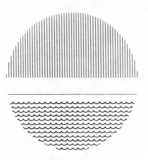

Temperature

Temperature is an important environmental variable. The simplicity of temperature measurement should not detract from its importance in environmental studies. Temperature directly affects the rate of biological activity. As temperature is increased 10°C within the tolerance range of a resting animal, the animal's physiological demands, as measured by oxygen consumption, will usually double. When an animal is in its temperature optimum, it is operating at maximum efficiency. Every species has an optimum and a lower and upper tolerance limit for temperature and, if given the chance, will make attempts to remain near the center of its range.

Some unique characteristics of standing water allow fishes to make their own temperature adjustments. Water forms temperature layers at different depths. Most of the sun's heat (or infrared rays) is absorbed in the first few inches of water. As a result, the surface waters are heated more and faster than the lower-lying waters. Water, like most substances, expands when heated. The expansion reduces the water's density (specific gravity) and, as a result, the warmer water weighs less per cubic centimeter than the cooler water. The surface waters then float on the lower-lying cool water. The difference between the warm surface water (epilimnion) and the cooler subsurface water (hypolimnion) can be very dramatic. These waters are often separated by a zone of rapidly dropping temperature, called the thermocline (literally, "temperature grade"). The thermocline can represent a change in temperature between the two layers of as much as 15°F (quite a shock for an unsuspecting swimmer). It usually forms an effective barrier to any circulation between the warm and cold layers (Figure 3–1). Fish, depending upon their optimum, will stay in the epilimnion (bluegills, largemouth (black) bass), or they will remain in the cold hypolimnion (trout, salmon). The fish take advantage of the different temperature layers and distribute themselves according to their optimum temperatures. In a deep, oligotrophic lake, there may be warm-water, cool-water, and cold-water fishes distributed by depth, all at near optimum temperatures.

The waters of the epilimnion and hypolimnion are separated (the lake is stratified or layered) early in the summer. Unless there is wind or other disturbance to break the stratification, the waters will remain separated all summer. As the weeks go by, the characteristics of the two layers begin to change. The epilimnion begins to lose plankton. Plankters die and fall towards the bottom, taking the nutrients tied up in their bodies with them. Because there is no circulation, there is no way for the nutrients of the epilimnion (warm surface water) to be replaced. The epilimnion becomes relatively clear, nutrient deficient, warm, and oxygenated.

The nature of the hypolimnion (cooler subsurface water) depends upon the basic nature of the lake. If it is a nutrient-rich (eutrophic) lake, the bacteria and other decomposers on the bottom will continue to feed on organic debris, using oxygen until oxygen levels of the bottom are very low. There is some local, very slow circulation, but the system is normally not in communication with the surface water. Trout, lake trout, salmon, and other cold-water fishes do not do well in such eutrophic lakes, because their temperature requirements dictate that they avoid the warm water, yet the cooler subsurface water is low in oxygen concentration. In oligotrophic lakes, the bottom water retains high oxygen concentrations because there is not much biological activity. The water tends to be nutrient deficient in these clear, basically sterile lakes, and the only marked difference between the epilimnion and the hypolimnion is temperature. Lake trout live at depths of hundreds of feet in such lakes.

The thermocline normally remains stable through the summer, until the cool temperatures and winds of fall break it up. The process is slow and involves mixing as the two layers become less distinct. At that time, the surface layer of temperate, eutrophic lakes receives nutrients from the hypolimnion. This nutrient mixing brings the necessary factors together for a fall plankton "bloom." When winter sets in, the entire lake is well mixed. Winter plankton populations never reach bloom proportions because no water stays very long in the lighted zone.

In the spring, the thermocline is established once again, and until the epilimnion is depleted of nutrients, a spring bloom is observed.

Oxygen and Carbon Dioxide

Temperature also has an effect on the amounts of dissolved gases, particularly oxygen, that water will hold. As the temperature decreases, the saturation level of oxygen increases. That is, cold water is able to hold more oxygen in solution than warm water. Solubility of oxygen is also greater in fresh water than in water with salts in solution.

The two sources of oxygen in a lake are: the surface exchange and plant production. Exchange of oxygen from the air is greatly enhanced by wave action and other disturbances. Plants produce oxygen only during photosynthesis (in the dark they consume oxygen). Because the sources of dissolved oxygen are in the surface waters, oxygen concentration plotted against depth often shows the same sort of profile as temperature (Figure 3–1, p. 38).

The earth's atmosphere is composed of slightly less than 20% oxygen, about 80% nitrogen, and the rest, various gases including carbon dioxide and ozone. In air, oxygen is in a gaseous state, while in water the gas is dissolved.

Because dissolved oxygen is in solution, there is less available to aquatic organisms, and it becomes a potentially limiting factor. Waters can become oxygen depleted in a short period of time, and they vary in their ability to hold oxygen.

Water can contain maximum amounts of dissolved oxygen when it is fresh and cold. Cold, freshwater streams can hold, at saturation, no more than 15 ppm (parts per million) of oxygen. The same temperature for sea water can contain about 12 ppm. Many species, such as mountain-stream fishes and open-ocean fishes require a constant flow of oxygen-saturated water, and will suffocate if not supplied with near saturation amounts. Most fishes can survive at concentrations above 4 ppm, and can exist comfortably at concentrations of 6 to 8 ppm. Some aquatic animals are adapted to survive at very low levels of oxygen. Most notable in this respect are the pollution-community insects, such as the larvae of midges, tubifex worms, and several flies (diptera). These organisms can live for a considerable length of time with no oxygen. Catfish and gars can survive near the lowest levels of oxygen concentration. They have adaptations to augment oxygen supply. Skin respiration, and air breathing (in which a bubble of air is held in the modified gas bladder, or stomach) are examples of such adaptations.

Oxygen is used in respiration as an essential element in the metabolic process of oxidation—a burning of fuel (food). The chemical structures of fats, carbohydrates, and proteins in the food contain long, high-energy, carbon chains. These carbon chains release energy as they are broken down into smaller units under the action of physiological enzyme systems. The resulting low-energy carbon is then combined with oxygen to produce carbon dioxide. Carbon dioxide acts as a means of carrying the waste, low-energy carbon, out of the animal's system. It is interesting to consider that mammalian systems do not regulate breathing rate according to a need for oxygen, but on a need to get rid of carbon dioxide dissolved in the bloodstream.

The carbon dioxide, aside from being a metabolic by-product and potentially a poison, is the source of raw material for the carbon compounds produced by plants. The flow of materials is cyclic. The plants take up carbon dioxide and give off oxygen. (Well-lighted, weedy ponds often have plants with an abundance of oxygen bubbles all over their surface, as the oxygen exceeds saturation levels.) The plants, in a sense, use up the animals' waste products. The animals, taking in oxygen and giving off carbon dioxide, seem to complete a cycle. The "balanced aquarium" is based on this cycle. At night both plants and animals use oxygen and give off carbon dioxide. During dark conditions, oxygen may become low and kill oxygen-sensitive organisms.

Carbonate Buffer System

Many chemicals not only dissolve in water, but form a family of dissolved compounds called a buffer system. For example, when carbon dioxide is dissolved in water, part of it forms carbonic acid, then part of the carbonic acid forms bicarbonate, which forms in part carbonate:

$$CO_2 + H_2O \rightleftharpoons H_2CO_3 \rightleftharpoons H^+ + HCO_3^- \rightleftharpoons 2H^+ + CO_3^=.$$

carbon water carbonic   bicarbonate   carbonate
dioxide   acid

In effect, the original carbon dioxide has spread itself, by changing form, through several compounds. Such an equilibrium condition works both ways: not only does the carbon dioxide change form and disperse through the total system, but when it evolves out of the system as a gas, it tends to be replaced by some of the chemicals moving back into carbon dioxide form (that is, as carbon dioxide is released as a gas, the equation moves to the left to replace the lost gas). Buffer systems, once established, tend to resist change.

Total Dissolved Solids

Materials in solution, called total dissolved solids (TDS), are important in agricultural situations. High levels of TDS produce growth problems in plants and are a problem in agriculture. The salts in the water damage agricultural plants by disrupting the internal salt/water balance. TDS can include a variety of salts, but is composed primarily of magnesium and calcium carbonates with various other salts present. TDS should not be confused with salinity, which is a term designating concentration of ocean salts. Sea salts exist in constant proportion, and are measured by a chlorinity ratio (Chap. 5). One of the constant problems facing international relations between the United States and Mexico is the TDS level of the Colorado River when it reaches Mexico.

Salts that are needed by plants and are often in short supply (tend to be limiting) are called nutrient salts. They are usually salts of sulfur, nitrogen, and phosphorus. Since plankton populations in nature are controlled by shortages of nutrient salts, the addition of such salts (including phosphate detergents) into water supplies by domestic sewage may cause plankton blooms. The plankton populations at bloom densities create other conditions that limit their population. They may be so thick that they shade all of the light, except for the first few centimeters of the water (possibly killing deeper-rooted aquatic plants), or their metabolic by-products may reach toxic proportions. A secondary effect of the bloom may be decreased oxygen levels (e.g., from decomposition of dead aquatic plants). The change in conditions then affects other resources such as fish, recreation, or domestic use.

The problem of artificial enrichment of streams and lakes is complex because it is difficult to decide when the enrichment has gone "too far." In lakes, nutrients are often taken up nearly as fast as they enter. The population builds up, producing organic decomposition with night and deep-water oxygen depletion.

Biochemical Oxygen Demand

The biochemical oxygen demand (BOD) test compares dissolved oxygen levels of the water to levels in the same water after 36 hours of storage in the dark. The drop in dissolved oxygen concentration, due to decomposition in the water, predicts the dissolved oxygen loss possible in natural waters. Thus BOD is a means of measuring the organic content and the potential of a system to develop low oxygen. The organic material (the high energy carbon chains that can be burned as fuel) that is suspended in the water will require oxygen to burn or oxidize. As the oxidation process takes place, oxygen is removed from the water reducing the total amount of dissolved oxygen present. A physiological strain is placed on other plants and animals in the water, sometimes producing kills. The higher forms of life are killed off, which allows simpler (and less desirable) forms to move in. Bacteria, fungi, and some resistant insects are predominant in such a pollution-oriented community.

Aquatic Habitats

Physiological and biological factors interact to form a gradient of habitat types that can be divided into general categories. The following models of such categories use aquatic situations:

Oligotrophic: these clean, deep lakes are typified by low nutrient levels and by an impervious substrate such as granite. They usually occur at high altitudes and the water is transparent. Conditions are constant throughout their depth, except for possible temperature stratification during warm months. Plankton species are diverse and sparse. Blooms rarely occur, because nutrients do not build up in the system. Dominant species are normally those of restricted niches (specialists) such as trout, cisco, and other deep cold-water fishes. In shallow waters, plants are scarce, and bottom-dwelling organisms are aquatic insect larvae (stonefly and mayfly nymphs, etc.).

Eutrophic: in contrast, these environments usually exist at lower elevations. Waters are nutrient rich, and fall and spring blooms are common when the thermocline turnover occurs. The bottom is typically rich in organic mud, and is oxygen deficient during stratification. Bottom forms are bacteria, fungi, and midge larvae. The basin is often of sedimentary material, which contributes nutrients to the lake. The conditions encountered during the seasonal changes are wide, and inhabitants, such as carp, catfish, and sunfish, are adapted for variable environments.

Mesotrophic: these intermediate types have differences in dissolved oxygen concentrations between the epilimnion and the hypolimnion, but the differences are not as drastic as in the eutrophic environment.

The waters below the lighted zone may be inhabited by shellfish and crustaceans for most of the year.

.A similar classification can be used for rivers and streams. A trout stream flowing over a granite bed has diverse larval insects and cold-water fishes, essentially oligotrophic conditions. A large, meandering, valley river is equivalent to a eutrophic lake. Temperature, turbidity, suspended sediment, and organic composition vary considerably in such a situation, but are usually high. The air/water interface provides aeration and, unless the river is very deep, oxygen will normally be in the 4 to 6 ppm range.

Man and Water

Man seems to affect aquatic systems in a typical way. It is as though man leaves his "print" in the form of dams, ponds, and straight-sided channels. He connects river drainage systems so that the unique biological characteristics of a system are obscured. He often introduces new species into drainage systems for recreation, for food, or by accident. As a result, many dominant fishes in lowland streams, lakes, and rivers are the same from coast to coast.

Water is a valuable resource, and has always been a primary consideration in any of man's endeavors. Water for transportation, agriculture, fishing, waste disposal, power, and recreation uses has stimulated construction near water—from a single cabin near a creek to a large city near a river. As a water resource is used, it is modified for maximum efficiency for the task at hand. Mill ponds, agricultural channels, flood by-passes, power and flood-control dams, all modify waters from their natural state.

While dams, channels, ponds and water diversion are necessary, the multiple-use concept of resource management dictates that several points of view be considered. Perhaps in view of the fact that some rivers are used entirely for industrial and domestic purposes, other rivers should be preserved to be used entirely for recreation, esthetics, and research (e.g., the wild-river program of the Pacific States). In any case, toxic materials and excesses of any use should be restricted. New methods for determining sewage contamination, such as the Millipore coliform technique (Chap. 15), allow anyone to conduct sewage contamination tests. Perhaps if more such procedures were available, more interested members of the public could participate in supervising the use of natural resources.

ECOLOGY LABORATORY

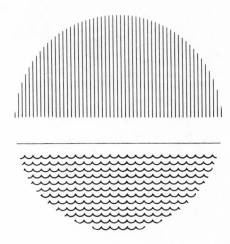

Frequently, a student in an aquatic biology course will respond with a "so what" when confronted with 8 ppm of oxygen. Although the aquatic ecosystem does not exist in separate parcels, we must measure it that way. The dilemma arises when the student learns that, in theory, the ecosystem is completely interrelated and that there can be no line of separation between any of its parts. Then he proceeds to the practical, where he measures isolated conditions using definite units, and fragments the newly learned ecosystem concept. The realities of the situation do not seem to bear out the theory. For a proper understanding of ecology, there must be a "systems" approach in the field as well as in the classroom. Rather than gather test results as though he were reading a set of dials, the student should use his results as glimpses of an overall situation. Data must be assembled as though each environment had its own personality. The environmental profile is a method of graphically visualizing such data as a system. It develops a holistic sense of ecology and helps to solve the student's dilemma. It is based on relationships and ranges of conditions, which are characteristic for particular environments (Chap. 15).

Water quality tests should be used to "read" an environment. It is important to approach an aquatic situation not simply to find out if it is "polluted." Each environment is unique, with its own set of contributing factors, such as depth, type of substrate, elevation, etc. The range of values likely to be encountered varies also. A rich (eutrophic) habitat will have a wider range of values for, say, temperature than many other environments. Thus it is less "sensitive" than, say, a high altitude, clear (oligotrophic) lake. Before environmental pollution (or the undesired change of an environment) can be evaluated, there must be a sense of the nature of each general "type" of environment. But still it must be appreciated that the types are guides for a wide diversity of aquatic situations, none exactly like any other.

Almost all of the following water quality tests are associated with two basic laboratory techniques:

Titration: a technique that uses volume measurement to represent the concentration of the substance to be measured. Traditionally, burettes (rather expensive and sensitive) have been used for titration.

In recent years, field kits have modified titrametric methods for use with dropper bottles and syringe-like devices. Burette determinations can be easily converted to dropper bottle titration. Standard droppers produce 15 drops per milliliter.

Colorimetry: a measurement of the substance under investigation by its optical properties. A color change occurs in proportion to the concentration of the chemical being measured. A photocell registers the change in color resulting from the test. The photocell activates a meter so that the concentration can be read directly, although sometimes concentrations must be translated from optical density, absorbence, or percent transmission. Color filters and other aids are used to increase the test accuracy.

These methods are measures of concentration—amounts of one thing in a particular weight or volume of something else. Units of measurement can be creatures per cubic meter as in plankton measurements, grams per liter (expressed as parts per thousand, o/oo) as in salinity, or milligrams per liter (expressed as parts per million, ppm) as in dissolved oxygen or free carbon dioxide.

Fluid Measurements

Measurements of fluids create some problems that should be considered before much work with fluids is attempted. All fluids interact with the surface of the container in which they are stored. Usually, the interaction is a surface attraction. The result is a curve of the surface water within the container, as the water "tries" to adhere to the sides of the container. In narrow-necked flasks, pipettes, burettes, or graduated cylinders, this curve is called a *meniscus* (see the figure below). In small tubes the meniscus may curve until it resembles a half-circle. The correct volume is always read at the lowest point of the curve.

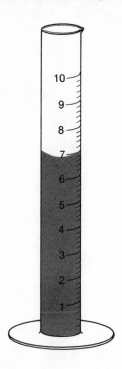

Graduated cylinder showing curved meniscus. For an accurate reading of volume, the meniscus is read at its lowest point.

Volumetric glassware should be used when procedures call for exact fluid measurements. A volumetric flask has a line indicating the volume (e.g., 1000 ml) calibrated and marked on a thin neck which minimizes possible error. Items of glassware, such as Erlenmeyer flasks, commonly have volumes painted on the side. These are not usually accurate. For approximate work, in which such marks are useful, it is recommended that the amount of fluid desired be measured with a graduated cylinder and poured into the flask. Then mark the flask with a file, glass stylus, or marking pencil.

Pipettes are normally marked TC (to contain) or TD (to deliver). TC pipettes are completely emptied by blowing and TD pipettes are held vertically, allowing the material to flow out. At the end of the flow of the TD pipette, the measured amount has been added, even though some material will be left in the pipette.

Laboratory Precautions

1. *Premeasured Glassware:* Premeasured Erlenmeyer flasks, scored at a level indicating approximate volume needed for titration, save considerable time. Volume measurements painted on the glassware at the factory should not be used without doublechecking. Often, such marks show considerable error. If high accuracy is required, measure the sample volume for each titration with a graduated cylinder or volumetric glassware.

2. *Dropper Calibration:* All dropper determinations assume "standard drop" titrations, and require droppers that produce 15 drops per ml. Droppers used in field determinations *should be checked* with a small graduated cylinder. If a dropper produces more or less than 15 drops per ml, *error can be substantial*. Use of a more accurate dropper should be considered.

3. *Contamination of Stock Reagents:* Stock solutions should be disturbed as little as possible. Clean glassware should be used to obtain amounts of reagents sufficient to make working solutions. After each test, all glassware should be rinsed to minimize error. When tests are completed, the working solutions should be discarded. This limits the possibility of contamination to the working solutions, allowing stock solutions to maintain maximum possible purity.

4. *Corrosive Chemicals:* When working in the laboratory, sulfuric acid should be used in a well-ventilated area, preferably under a hood. It and other corrosives, such as sodium hydroxide, should be treated with extreme caution. Anyone using such chemicals should know location of a freshwater outlet. In the event of contact with skin or eyes, the area should immediately be flushed thoroughly.

5. *Accuracy/Precision:* When conducting a test for the first few times, results may be erratic, particularly in a sensitive test, such as the Winkler Oxygen Determination. With continued practice, lab technique improves and close repeatability of results is obtained. Repeatability of results is roughly equivalent to precision. On the other hand, accuracy is roughly equivalent to how close the test results actually come to the concentration of the factor being measured (Discussion of precision/accuracy can be found in *Standard Methods*, 1971: 22 and Sokal and Rohlf, 1969).

6. An additional precaution should be added. You do not get something for nothing. If the inexpensive kit methods did as good a job as *Standard Methods,* the professional water quality labs would be using them. A technique that offers simple testing procedures must then be expected to yield approximate results. In many of the tests, we have provided several alternatives for testing a single environmental factor. It is hoped that with practice and experience in environmental evaluation, more difficult but authoritative tests will be conducted. The next

step is for those who would pursue the study of environmental biology to the level at which resource management is influenced. A trio of books is suggested: Odum (1971), to continue the development of basic principles of Part I; *Standard Methods* (1971), to continue development of sophistication of chemical techniques (*Standard Methods* outlines techniques that are acceptable for determinations to see if conditions are meeting the letter of the law); and *Biometry* by Sokal and Rohlf (1969), a book on statistical design, to continue the development of insight into sampling and design of testing programs.

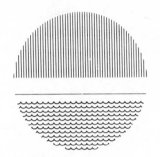

3. Temperature

Temperature is probably the most important environmental condition. Aside from its direct effect on physiological processes, it has a great effect on the standing waters of lakes, ponds, and oceans by its tendency to form temperature layers (Chap. 2). Surface waters warm first, and as they warm they expand and become lighter than the cold underlying water. The warm surface water floats on the cooler water separated by a narrow, rapidly cooling transition zone called a thermocline. The isolation of the water above the thermocline (epilimnion) is often complete. The characteristics of the epilimnion may be so different from those of the hypolimnion (below the thermocline) that the two may act as different categories of lakes (Chap. 14). For example, nutrient depletion of the epilimnion may cause it to act like oligotrophic water, while the hypolimnion may reflect a true eutrophic or mesotrophic condition. Any survey of stand-

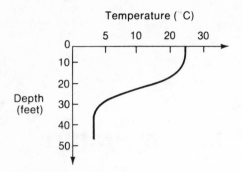

Temperature (°C)

Figure   3–1   Depth/Temperature.   In first 15 feet, the water is very warm. From 15 to 35 feet (thermocline), the water changes from 24° to 4°C. Below the thermocline, water is cold.

ing water should first determine the presence of a thermocline, and should make subsequent evaluations with respect to it.

For purposes of visualizing the temperature profile and for convenience in assigning values for other tests, a plot of temperature against depth is valuable (Figure 3–1).

MATERIALS

1. Thermometer
2. Water sampler

Thermocline Determination

PROCEDURE:

1. Take temperature of the surface water and record.
2. Lower the sampler to the bottom (or the end of the line in a deep lake). Record depth.
3. Bring a sample of bottom water to the surface.
4. Take the temperature of the bottom water sample. If the temperature differs more than a few degrees from step 1, a thermocline probably exists. Continue to step 5. If there is no difference, the water is mixed, and there is no thermocline.
5. Lower the sampler to a depth of about one-half the depth of step 2.

6. Bring a sample to the surface and record temperature.
7. If the temperature is approximately that of surface water, the half-depth is above the thermocline. Sample and take temperature in steps of a few feet, starting at the half-depth level. Work deeper until a dramatic temperature change (1°C or more per meter) is observed, indicating a thermocline.
8. If the temperature is nearer the bottom reading, the thermocline is above the half-depth level, and the step-wise temperature sampling should proceed upward of half-depth, until the thermocline is encountered.
9. Plot depth/temperature (Figure 3–1).

NOTE:

If no large ponds or other suitable bodies of water are available, a thermocline can be established in an aquarium.

If an aquarium heater is placed in a tank with no agitation in the form of bubblers or filters, soon there will be a warm-water lens floating on the top. The temperature system can be measured by slowly lowering a chemical thermometer into the water and recording the temperature in steps of 3.0 cm intervals. Dramatic visualization of the isolation of the epilimnion can be achieved by carefully dropping food coloring into the water. The hypolimnion, thermally isolated, stays clear.

Measurement of temperature for scientific purposes normally uses the centigrade scale (°C).

4. Turbidity and Visibility

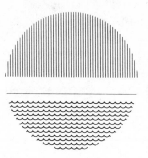

The terms turbidity, visibility, and transparency are roughly equivalent, but there is some distinction made between visual and mechanical methods of measurement. Visual methods involve a decision on the part of the operator as to when an object, such as a Secchi disc or a candle, is no longer visible through the water to be tested. Mechanical methods are colorimetry (Chap. 2) or some variation of it.

The standard unit of measurement of turbidity is the Jackson Turbidity Unit. It is obtained through the use of a Jackson Candle Turbidimeter or a colorimeter. The turbidimeter measures the height of a column of test water necessary to filter out the image of a standard candle. It is useful only in rather turbid waters.

In situations of high transparency, or in field applications, the Secchi disc is used. Units are recorded in meters or feet, and are referred to, by convention, as Secchi Transparency.

Turbidity, usually the result of suspended particles in the water, is most often caused by silt or other soil particles, dead plant fragments, or living plants such as phytoplankton. Under some conditions, plant pigments can stain the water and also decrease the transparency.

Under turbid conditions, light penetration is reduced, decreasing the depth of the growing zone. Susceptible organisms (those adapted for clear water conditions) may be affected by buildup of particles on gills and other structures. Like temperature, the simplicity of turbidity measurement (Secchi Disc) should not detract from its importance.

Secchi Disc Transparency

PROCEDURE:

1. The disc should be attached to a premeasured line so that the black and white quadrants are facing the experimenter.
2. Lower the disc into the water until it disappears from view.
3. Record the depth of the disc by noting the water level on the line.
4. Lower the disc a few more inches.
5. Slowly raise the disc until it is again visible.
6. Again record the depth of the disc.

CALCULATIONS:

1. Average the two readings for Secchi Disc Transparency.
2. Secchi Disc Transparency is expressed in meters or feet.

LIMITATIONS:

1. Influenced by the subjective impressions of the experimenter.
2. Best results are obtained in bright sunlight.

MATERIALS
1. Secchi disc
2. Line marked at regular intervals

Turbidity by Colorimetry

```
┌─────────────────────────┐
│       MATERIALS         │
│  1. Colorimeter         │
│  2. Colorimeter tubes   │
└─────────────────────────┘
```

PROCEDURE:

1. Place a colorimeter tube of distilled water* in the light cell. This is used for calibration and is called a blank.
2. Press the light switch and adjust the meter for a reading of zero.
3. Replace the blank with a water sample.
4. Press the light switch and read the turbidity in Jackson Turbidity Units, or consult a standardization curve for turbidity in JTU.

TEST MECHANICS:

1. The colorimeter is designed so that the sample is placed between the light source and a photocell.
2. The blank establishes the amount of light attenuated (absorbed and scattered) by the water. This establishes the zero reference point.
3. In the sample, any additional attenuation of light is due to turbidity and is read directly from the meter or determined from the standardization curve in Jackson Turbidity Units.

Jackson Candle Turbidimeter

```
┌─────────────────────────┐
│       MATERIALS         │
│  1. Jackson Candle      │
│     Turbidimeter        │
│     a. A graduated glass│
│        cylinder         │
│     b. Standard candle  │
│     c. Support for candle│
│        and glass cylinder│
└─────────────────────────┘
```

PROCEDURE:

1. Place a standard candle in the base of the turbidimeter.
2. Place the graduated glass cylinder in the holder above the candle.
3. Dim the light in the room.

_____

* If the sample water is colored, it should be filtered and the filtered sample used in place of the distilled water blank.

4. Light the candle and begin pouring the sample water into the graduated cylinder while viewing the candle from above and directly through the column of water.
5. Pour slowly until the image of the candle disappears.
6. The turbidity value in Jackson Turbidity Units may be read directly from the meniscus of the water level in the graduated cylinder.

TEST MECHANICS:

A candle turbidimeter measures the length of the light path through the sample to be tested. The turbidity of the sample is determined by the amount of liquid required to cause the image of a standard candle to disappear when viewed directly through the column of test water.

TEST LIMITATIONS:

1. The turbidimeter may be used to measure turbidity between 25 and 1000 units. For values greater than 1000, the sample must be diluted with distilled water until the value falls below 1000. The results must then be expanded by the dilution factor (e.g., if diluted twice the volume, results must be multiplied by two).
2. The candle wick must be trimmed, and the candle kept in position by a well-oiled spring.
3. The candle should only burn a few minutes. Longer duration will cause the flame to increase in size and brightness.

INTERFERENCES:

1. Sediments which settle out quickly.
2. Scratched, dirty, or sooty glassware.
3. Air bubbles.
4. Air drafts.

BLANKS

In many tests, the presence of the testing system itself will produce an effect on the test results. Indicators of pH may change pH, or chemicals used to produce a clear end point in a titration may cause the end point to appear later than it should for a correct titration. In colorimetry, different sample waters will have optical properties that will be reflected in a different reading if just the sample water is placed in the colorimeter.

Tests are usually designed to measure only one thing. Since there are many sources of potential error in the water or chemicals being used, a procedure has been developed that is designed to offset these influences. Normally, the influence is measured, then subtracted from the measuring system, so that the net effect of the influence is zero. Such an operation is called the determination of a blank. In some cases, it is very simple, such as zeroing the meter on a colorimetric test. In other cases, involved chemical blank determination tests must be made.

5. Chloride Ion and Other Salts

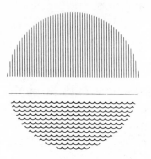

The concentration of salts in solution is critical to proper plant growth (Chap. 2). Salts in solution also affect taste and general suitability of drinking water. Chloride may appear in fresh waters as a result of salt deposits in the ground dissolving into the fresh water, or as salts left after evaporation, particularly in irrigation water. Intrusion of ocean salts, moving by tidal action into river systems, is a problem in coastal areas.

Ocean salts occur in a constant proportion which allows chlorinity to be used as an index of all the salts present. In any ocean water at any dilution, chloride ions represent about 50.4% of total salts present. If chloride determinations are multiplied by 1.8,* an approximation of total ocean salinity is obtained.

---

*Complete formula: $S(o/oo) = 0.03 + 1.805 \, Cl \, (o/oo)$ (Dietrich, 1963: 50).

Chloride Ion Test

BURETTE TITRATION METHOD

Step 1   pH Check

The pH of the solution being tested must be within the range of 7–10.

pH PROCEDURE:

1. Tear a 1″ strip of wide range pH paper.
2. Dip the paper into a 100 ml sample. Compare the color of the strip with the pH color ranges on the dispenser.
3. Read the pH.
4. If the pH is not within the 7–10 range, adjust the pH by adding, dropwise, NaOH to raise the pH, H_2SO_4 to lower it.

MATERIALS

1. Wide range pH paper
2. Solutions (in dropper bottles):
   a. 1 N Sodium hydroxide (NaOH)
   b. 1 N Sulfuric acid (H_2SO_4)

Step 2   Standardization of Silver Nitrate Titrant

To maintain accuracy of titration, standardization of the silver nitrate solution must be made. If the solution is kept from light, restandardization need not be done for several weeks.

STANDARDIZATION PROCEDURE:

1. Pour 40 ml of sodium chloride (NaCl) solution into a 100 ml flask.
2. Pipette 1.0 ml of potassium chromate solution to the NaCl solution.
3. Fill the burette with silver nitrate ($AgNO_3$) solution. Free the burette of air bubbles. Record the level of the $AgNO_3$ in the burette.

MATERIALS

1. 100 ml Erlenmeyer flask
2. 50 ml graduated cylinder
3. 50 ml burette, stand, and clamp for silver nitrate titration
4. 1.0 ml pipette
5. Solutions:
   a. 0.0141 N Sodium Chloride (NaCl)
   b. 0.0141 N Silver Nitrate ($AgNO_3$)
   c. Potassium Chromate indicator

4. Titrate with $AgNO_3$.* A white precipitate will form. Continue titrating until a pink-orange end point is reached. Both the precipitate and the solution should assume the end point color.
5. Record the number of ml of $AgNO_3$ used.
6. Calculate the normality (N') of the $AgNO_3$ using the following equation:**

$$\frac{(0.564)}{\text{ml of } AgNO_3 \text{ used}} = N'$$

Step 3   Titration of Water Sample

TITRATION PROCEDURE:

1. Run the water sample up to the 100 ml scored mark on the flask. If a lot of suspended matter is in the sample pass it through filter paper in a glass funnel.
2. Add 1.0 ml of potassium chromate solution.
3. Fill the burette with silver nitrate ($AgNO_3$) solution.* Free the burette of air bubbles. Record the level of the $AgNO_3$ solution in the burette.
4. Titrate the sample with $AgNO_3$. Gently swirl the flask and continue titrating until a pink-orange end point is reached. Both the precipitate and the solution should assume the end point color.
5. Record the new level of $AgNO_3$ and calculate the difference between the two $AgNO_3$ readings (discard unused $AgNO_3$).

MATERIALS

1. 250 ml Erlenmeyer flask scored at 100 ml volume
2. 50 ml burette, stand, and clamp for silver nitrate titration
3. 1.0 ml pipette
4. Solutions: same as Step 2

---

*$AgNO_3$ must be kept out of the light to avoid photographic reaction. Once the reagent is poured from the bottle, do not return it to the stock bottle.

**Derived from the relation $NV = N'V'$, where N and V = known normality and volume of NaCl and V' = known volume of $AgNO_3$. The equation is then solved for N' to determine the normality of $AgNO_3$.

CALCULATIONS:

The following equation must be used to calculate parts per million (ppm) of chloride ion present in the water sample. The chemical characteristics of the indicator (potassium chromate) produces a blank (Chap. 4). We are estimating the blank at 0.2 ml in the following equation. Directions for the determination of the exact blank may be found in *Standard Methods* (1971: 96).

$$\text{ppm of chloride ion} = (A - 0.2) \times N \times 354.5$$

A = ml of $AgNO_3$ titrant used
0.2 = blank attributed to the potassium chromate
N = normality of the $AgNO_3$ figured in step 2
354.5 = constant

TEST MECHANICS:

The silver from the silver nitrate combines with the chloride being measured to form a white precipitate. When the chloride is used up, the silver is free to combine with the chromate indicator to produce a pink-orange end point, silver chromate.

NOTE:

For marine situations much higher concentrations of $AgNO_3$ are necessary. Such high concentrations are less stable than the concentrations used here. The use of other methods such as hydrometers or conductivity meters are indicated except for exact work.

The accuracy of this determination depends on the standardization of the silver nitrate titrant. Therefore, to obtain maximum accuracy possible, the use of burette measurement or volumetric glassware is recommended.

TITRATION

In many water quality tests, chemical reactions are used. The amount of chemical necessary to "use up" or complete a reaction often tells us the concentration of a substance in the sample. For example, in the dissolved oxygen test, iodine is substituted for oxygen. Then the amount of thiosulfate needed to "use up" all of the iodine tells us how much oxygen was originally in the solution. Titrations are done using a burette (a slender glass tube with measurements of volume marked down its length). A valve at the bottom (usually a stopcock) allows closely controlled amounts to be released into a measured volume of sample. When the reaction is complete, something "happens"—usually a color change or precipitate. This "happening" is the end point. There are ways of determining when the end point is near. Usually the end point reaction will occur in the immediate vicinity of the titrant as it goes into the solution. Then, as the solution is swirled, the reaction (i.e., color change, precipitate, etc.) vanishes. This should serve as a warning to decrease the rate of titration. When the end point is reached, the stopcock is closed, and the amount of chemical used to reach that end point is recorded, and translated into amounts of substance (i.e., oxygen) that was in the original sample.

Tests for Chloride Ion and Other Salts

A. HYDROMETER

The addition of salt to fresh water does not measurably increase the volume, but it does increase the weight. The result is an increase in specific gravity. If a sealed glass tube weighted to approximately the density of water (1 g/ml) is placed in a fluid of unknown specific gravity, it will float high if the fluid is heavier than water, and it will float low if the fluid is lighter than water. Such a glass tube with a calibrated stem is called a hydrometer. It gives a rough approximation of specific gravity. Because this method is not sensitive, its use is restricted to brackish or marine waters.

Hydrometers are available, calibrated in parts per thousand (o/oo) salinity from scientific supply houses.

B. CONDUCTIVITY AS A MEASURE OF IONS IN SOLUTION

Distilled water will not conduct an electrical current. If ions, or the dissolved form of ionic compounds, such as NaCl, are added to such water, they will act as conductors. As the concentration of such ionic materials increases, the ability of the solution to conduct an electrical current also increases. Thus, the amounts of ions in solution can be determined by the tendency of the solution to conduct an electrical current.

Conductivity devices range from simple Wheatstone bridges to complex instruments that are self-compensating for temperature, polarization, and other variables. The main advantage of the expensive equipment is that it allows direct reading in salinity units of parts per thousand (o/oo) under a variety of situations, while more simple equipment reads in units of conductance and must be calibrated using known standards to determine salinity.

Saline waters contain high concentrations of several kinds of ions. Measurements of gross levels of dissolved salt solutions are not technically difficult, and instruments can be read directly. Determination of hardness, on the other hand, even with good instruments, requires calibration for accuracy. This is because of the relatively low concentrations of ions in fresh water, and because of the non-linear response of conductivity to dissolved salts. Alkalinity, pH, or the presence of certain salts will produce errors at such concentrations.

Kit Methods

Biological and chemical supply companies (App.) offer chloride ion test kits. These kits combine convenience with relatively low cost. The extensive equipment involved in the titration method and the insensitivity of the hydrometer method may make the kits a more practical compromise.

6. Buffer Systems in Water

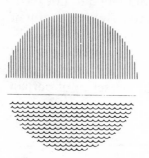

Buffers are systems that tend to resist certain kinds of changes. The carbonate system (Chap. 2) is an example of a chemical buffer system that occurs commonly in natural waters. It is composed of carbon dioxide and ions of bicarbonate and carbonate in solution. The relative proportions of each of these compounds tend to remain constant. If the concentration of one component in the system is changed, the "balancing effect" of the buffer system tends to counteract this change. The ions redistribute themselves to restore the original proportions.

Characteristics of pH are moderated by buffers. The pH scale (0 to 14) is a means of measuring the level of acidity or basidity of a solution. Acids are low in pH, and are measured by the amounts of hydrogen ions (H^+) that the acid liberates into solution. A strong acid, such as HCl (stomach acid), liberates virtually all of its hydrogen ions.

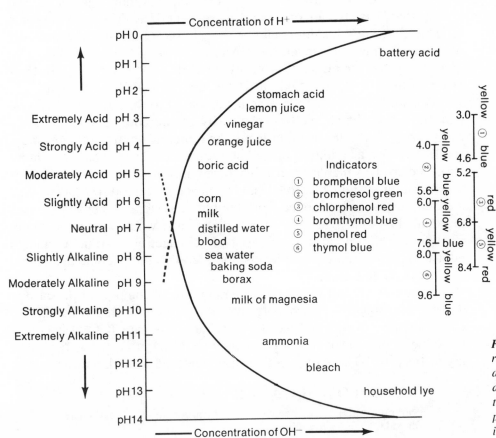

Figure 6–1 *pH scale. A curve showing relative amounts of hydroxide ion (OH^-) and hydrogen ion (H^+). Appropriate indicators to cover pH range within extremes are indicated on the right. For perspective, the pH of familiar materials is indicated throughout the curve.*

The HCl goes to Cl^- and H^+. Acetic acid (vinegar), a weak acid, releases relatively few of its hydrogen ions. When the amount of H^+ in solution is measured, an index of acidity is obtained. (Bases (OH^-) react similarly. For example, a strong base, NaOH, ionizes to form Na^+ and OH^-.) A solution with a pH of 7 is neutral, less than 7 is acidic, and greater than 7 is alkaline or basic (Figure 6–1). If acidity is the presence of H^+ in the water, alkalinity can be thought of as the tendency to accept or "cancel" those hydrogen ions. Another way of looking at this is to imagine the H^+ being neutralized by an OH^- ($H^+ + OH^- \rightarrow HOH$ or H_2O). If there is a lot of OH^- in water, the pH is high or alkaline.

If a solution of a simple base is compared to that of a buffered system, the pH of the simple base can easily be altered by the addition of a neutralizing acid. On the other hand, the buffered solution remains more stable, because as addition of acid neutralizes the base in solution, more base becomes available from other forms in the system, as in the carbonate buffer system. Carbonate and bicarbonate act as OH^-, but as they are neutralized and removed from the buffer system, the system makes more alkaline ions available. In fact, this is just what happens in blood. If buffers in the blood did not resist pH change, every time an animal built up high carbon dioxide levels, the blood would become acidic and damage delicate tissues.

Conditions found in natural waters involve a complex of the carbon dioxide—carbonate—bicarbonate system, together with the associated characteristics of pH and hardness. When carbonate ($CO_3^=$) becomes available to neutralize the carbonic acid (H_2CO_3), it is said to be "moving to the left." The situation is best understood as a chemical system:

$$CO_2 + H_2O \rightleftharpoons H_2CO_3 \rightleftharpoons H^+ + HCO_3^- \rightleftharpoons 2H^+ + CO_3^=$$

carbon   water   carbonic   bicarbonate   carbonate
dioxide   acid

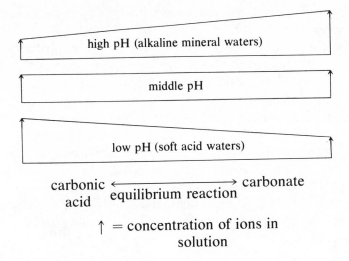

carbonic ⟷ carbonate
acid equilibrium reaction

↑ = concentration of ions in
solution

For example, in highly organic waters there is high concentration of carbon dioxide due to biological activity. Because the emphasis is on the left end of the buffer system, CO_2 is high and $CO_3^=$ is low. The water is not hard (it is "soft"). The softness is caused by the abundant organic molecules present under these conditions chemically interacting with the hardness-producing magnesium and calcium ions (Hynes, 1970: 43). The presence of CO_2 and other organic acids in high concentrations creates low pH (4 to 6). The total result is the "soft-acid" water found in bogs, swamps, and much of the water of the Atlantic Coastal Plain. The so called "black water" of these habitats results from the stain produced by plant pigments. On the other hand, water flowing through limestone, gypsum, and other carbonate salts (mineral waters) has chemical emphasis on the right end of the system, with resultant high (basic) pH and hardness. The pH of both soft acid and mineral waters would be more extreme, if it were not for the buffering effect of the carbonate system.

The calcium carbonate ($CaCO_3$) fraction also contributes to hardness, and to the concentration of dissolved salts measured in parts per million (ppm). In early water quality work, one test for hardness used the amount of a standard soap solution necessary to produce suds in the sample. The hardness (primarily calcium and magnesium ions) in the water precipitated the soap until the ions were used up. Then, any additional soap would produce suds. Hardness was measured by the amount of soap necessary to get to the suds end point. The best current test for hardness, the EDTA method (App.), uses the same principle but it is based on chemicals which form complexes with the dissolved salts. Its end point is a color change from red to blue. It is measured in terms of equivalent concentrations of calcium carbonate.

Free Carbon Dioxide Tests

A. BURETTE TITRATION METHOD

PROCEDURE:

1. Collect the water sample in a sampler that will prevent contact between the water sample and the air. Record the water temperature and the time of collection. Run the sample up to the 100 ml mark scored on the flask. Avoid agitating the sample.
2. Add 10 drops of phenolphthalein indicator to the sample. If the sample turns faint pink to red, there is no carbon dioxide present. If the sample remains colorless, continue to step 3.
3. Fill the burette with sodium hydroxide (NaOH) solution. Free the burette of air bubbles. Record the level of the NaOH in the burette.
4. Titrate the sample with NaOH over a white background. Gently

---

MATERIALS

1. Water sampler
2. Thermometer
3. 250 ml Erlenmeyer flask scored at 100 ml volume
4. Burette, stand, and clamp for sodium hydroxide titration
5. Solutions:
   a. Phenolphthalein indicator
   b. 0.0227 N Sodium hydroxide (NaOH)

swirl the flask and continue titrating until a faint pink color (viewed through the side of the flask) persists for 5–30 seconds. Good lighting is necessary because of the faint color of the end point.
5. Record the new level of the NaOH and then calculate the difference between the two NaOH readings.
6. Multiply the ml of NaOH used by 10 to yield free carbon dioxide in ppm (If 60 ml sample bottle is used, multiply by 16.65).

TEST MECHANICS:

Free carbon dioxide dissolved in water acts as an acid. The H^+ that is produced is neutralized by NaOH. When all of the H^+ is neutralized, continued titration with NaOH turns the solution basic producing a faint pink phenolphthalein reaction. The amount of NaOH needed to produce the pink color is equivalent to the amount of carbon dioxide that was in the solution.

LIMITATIONS:

Maximum precision and accuracy possible with this technique is plus or minus 10% (*Standard Methods,* 1971: 94). Error increases with approximate methods such as dropper bottle titration. Sources of error include:

a. NaOh picks up water and carbon dioxide from the air.
b. The end point determination is subjective.
c. Loss of some carbon dioxide is encountered if the sample is transported, stored for any length of time, or agitated.

B. Dropper Bottle Titration Method for Field Use

PROCEDURE:

1. Collect the water sample in a sampler that will prevent contact between the water sample and the air. Record the water temperature and the time of collection.
2. Run the sample up to the 50 ml scored mark on the flask. Avoid agitating the sample.
3. Add 5 drops of phenolphthalein indicator to the sample. If the sample turns faint pink to red, there is no carbon dioxide present. If the sample remains colorless, continue to step 4.
4. Add drops of sodium hydroxide (NaOH) to the sample. There will be a temporary local pink color as the NaOH enters the sample. Count and record the number of drops necessary to produce a faint pink to red color (viewed through the side of the flask) which persists for 5–30 seconds. For the best results, work over a white background with good lighting.
5. The number of drops of NaOH is equivalent to free carbon dioxide concentration in ppm. If 15 drops is more or less than 1 ml, an error will be introduced.

pH Tests

A. Colorimetric Determination Methods

pH Papers

PROCEDURE:

1. Tear a 1″ strip of paper from the wide range dispenser.
2. Dip the paper into the water sample.

MATERIALS

1. Water sampler
2. Thermometer
3. 100 ml Erlenmeyer flask scored at 50 ml volume
4. Solutions (in plastic dropping bottles: 15 drops/ml):
   a. Phenolphthalein indicator
   b. 0.0171 N Sodium hydroxide (NaOH)

MATERIALS

1. Set of pH papers
   wide range
   narrow range

3. Compare the color of the pH paper with the pH chart on the side of dispenser.
4. Based on the approximate reading of the wide range paper, select a narrow range pH paper.
5. Dip a 1″ strip of narrow range paper into the water sample.
6. Compare colors and read pH.

Color Comparator

PROCEDURE:

1. Fill each of two sample tubes with 4–5 ml of the water sample to be tested.
2. Add 4–6 drops of wide range pH indicator to one of the tubes and swirl.
3. Place this tube in the viewing chamber of the color comparator.
4. Place the second untreated tube of water (the blank) in a position behind the color standards of the comparator, in order to provide equal light intensity.
5. Hold comparator up to a light source. Compare the sample color to the color of the standards. Read pH from standard having color closest to that of the sample.

MATERIALS
1. Color comparator
2. Sample tubes
3. Indicator solution

pH by Colorimeter

PROCEDURE:

1. Fill a colorimeter tube with 25 ml of the sample.
2. Add 1 ml of wide range indicator. Swirl to mix.
3. Fill another colorimeter tube with 25 ml of the original sample. This is used for calibration and is referred to as a blank.
4. Place the blank in the colorimeter, check that proper filter is in

MATERIALS
1. Colorimeter
2. Colorimeter tubes
3. Wide range pH indicator
4. pH scale
5. Filter

place, press the light switch and adjust the meter for a reading of zero.

5. Replace the blank with the water sample.
6. Press the light switch and read the pH.

TEST MECHANICS:

Indicators are chemicals that produce a color change with pH changes. The pH can be determined by measuring or comparing the color. Process is exaggerated by a color filter.

LIMITATIONS:

1. Samples should be tested as quickly as possible. Biological activity can alter pH values.
2. Colorimetric methods are approximate. Interferences may be a result of: sample color, turbidity, temperature, or salinity.

B. ELECTROMETRIC DETERMINATION

Electrometric methods of pH determination are superior to colorimetric methods. Colorimetry is subject to interference from several sources, including water color, turbidity, colloidal matter, chlorine, and other oxidizing and reducing agents. In testing nonbuffered water, the pH indicator itself may influence pH.

Recent improvements in pH meters include glass electrodes which are relatively free from interference. The principle of the electrode is based on the fact that at constant temperature, a pH change will produce a corresponding change in the electrical property of the solution. The glass electrode, immersed in the sample, will read accurately in the middle pH ranges. By the application of special devices or tables available from the manufacturers, extremes of pH can be read with a fair degree of accuracy. Depending upon conditions, the sample may need agitation in the vicinity of the electrode.

The instruments are expensive, and require constant attention to possible causes of low performance: weak batteries and cracked, plugged, or fouled electrodes. For accurate work, they require frequent standardization with buffer solutions of known pH. For the teaching field biologist, the colorimetric methods, though less accurate, are adequate without the initial expense and technical maintenance necessary with the electrometric method.

Alkalinity Tests

Chemical determination (titration) of hydroxides, carbonates, and bicarbonates in water samples.

PHENOLPHTHALEIN ALKALINITY

Burette Titration Method

Determination of hydroxide ions (OH^-) and free carbonates. Shows readily available alkaline ions.

PROCEDURE:

1. Run the sample up to the 100 ml scored mark on the flask.
2. Add 5 drops of phenolphthalein indicator to the sample. If the sample remains colorless, there are few hydroxides or free carbonates present. If the sample turns faint pink to red, continue to step 3.
3. Fill the burette with sulfuric acid (H_2SO_4) solution. Free the burette of air bubbles. Record the level of the H_2SO_4 in the burette.
4. Titrate the sample with sulfuric acid over a white background.

MATERIALS

1. 250 ml Erlenmeyer flask scored at 100 ml volume
2. Burette, stand, and clamp for sulfuric acid titration
3. Solutions:
   a. Phenolphthalein indicator
   b. 0.02 N Sulfuric acid (H_2SO_4)

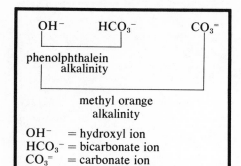

OH⁻ = hydroxyl ion
HCO₃⁻ = bicarbonate ion
CO₃⁼ = carbonate ion

Subtracting phenolphthalein alkalinity from methyl orange (or total) alkalinity indicates distribution of alkalinity through the buffer system.

MATERIALS

1. 250 ml Erlenmeyer flask scored at 100 ml volume
2. Burette, stand, and clamp for sulfuric acid titration
3. Solutions:
   a. Methyl orange indicator
   b. 0.02 N Sulfuric acid (H_2SO_4)

Gently swirl the flask and continue titrating until the pink color (viewed through the side of the flask) just disappears.

5. Record the new level of the H_2SO_4 and then calculate the difference between the two H_2SO_4 readings.
6. Multiply the ml of sulfuric acid used by 10 to yield phenolphthalein alkalinity in ppm of $CaCO_3$.

METHYL ORANGE (OR TOTAL) ALKALINITY

Burette Titration Method

Shows readily available alkalinity (i.e., the phenolphthalein alkalinity, which is OH⁻, and free carbonates), in addition to total carbonates and bicarbonates.

PROCEDURE:

1. Run the sample up to the 100 ml scored mark on the flask.
2. Add 5 drops of methyl orange indicator to the sample. If the sample remains orange, there is no alkalinity. If the sample turns yellow, it is alkaline: there may be hydroxides, and/or carbonates, and/or bicarbonates. Continue to step 3.
3. Fill the burette with sulfuric acid (H_2SO_4) solution. Free the burette of air bubbles. Note the level of the sulfuric acid in the burette.
4. Titrate the sample with H_2SO_4 over a white background. Gently swirl the flask and continue titrating until sample just changes from a pure yellow. Slowly continue titrating until a faint orange tint appears (the end point).
5. Record the new level of the H_2SO_4 and then calculate the difference between the two H_2SO_4 readings.
6. Multiply the ml of sulfuric acid used by 10 to yield methyl orange alkalinity in ppm of $CaCO_3$.

TEST MECHANICS:

Hydroxide, carbonate, and bicarbonate ions are alkaline and turn phenolphthalein pink and methyl orange yellow. The addition of sulfuric acid neutralizes the alkaline substances. Continued titration with sulfuric acid turns the solution acidic which produces a colorless phenolphthalein end point. The methyl orange end point is an orange tint, and occurs at a lower pH than phenolphthalein. At the methyl orange end point, all of the alkaline reserves are exhausted. The amount of sulfuric acid needed to produce the methyl orange end point is proportional to the amount of alkaline materials in that sample.

LIMITATIONS:

1. Test should be run as soon as possible after collection.
2. Chlorine, sample color, and turbidity can alter test results.
3. For very low (≤ 10 ppm) conditions of alkalinity, special techniques are needed (*Standard Methods,* 1971: 55).

PHENOLPHTHALEIN ALKALINITY

Dropper Bottle Method for Field Use

PROCEDURE:

1. Run the sample up to the 50 ml scored mark on the flask.
2. Add 3 drops of phenolphthalein to the sample. If the sample remains colorless, there are few hydroxides or available carbonates present. If the sample turns faint pink to red, continue to step 3.
3. Add drops of sulfuric acid (H_2SO_4) to the sample. Count and record the number of drops that makes the faint pink color just disappear.
4. Each drop of H_2SO_4 is equivalent to 5 ppm of $CaCO_3$. If 15 drops is more or less than 1 ml, an error will be introduced.

EQUIVALENTS IN $CaCO_3$

Alkalinity determinations test for all of the forms of the carbonate buffer system: bicarbonate, carbonate, and hydroxide. For convenience in expressing the results of the total system, alkalinity is expressed in ppm $CaCO_3$ of phenolphthalein alkalinity or methyl orange alkalinity, even though in actuality the alkalinity may be distributed between hydroxide, bicarbonate, and carbonate. The relationship between carbonates and the other forms of alkalinity is termed equivalence.

Another form of equivalence is in hardness. Hardness in water is really a combination of many salts in solution, including magnesium, calcium, and others. But their presence is evaluated in terms of what their concentration would be if they were calcium carbonate. Even though there might be little $CaCO_3$ present, what is there is measured in equivalents of $CaCO_3$.

MATERIALS

1. 100 ml Erlenmeyer flask scored at 50 ml volume
2. Solutions (in dropper bottles: 15 drops/ml):
   a. Phenolphthalein indicator
   b. 0.075 N Sulfuric acid (H_2SO_4)

Methyl Orange (or Total) Alkalinity

Dropper Bottle Method for Field Use

PROCEDURE:

1. Run the sample up to the 50 ml scored mark on the flask.
2. Add 3 drops of methyl orange indicator to the sample. If the sample remains orange, there is no alkalinity. If the sample turns yellow, it is alkaline: there may be hydroxides, and/or carbonates, and/or bicarbonates. Continue to step 3.
3. Add drops of sulfuric acid (H_2SO_4) to the sample. Count and note the number of drops necessary until the sample just changes from a pure yellow. Slowly continue titrating until a faint orange tint appears (end point).
4. Each drop of H_2SO_4 is equivalent to 5 ppm of $CaCO_3$. If 15 drops is more or less than 1 ml, an error will be introduced.

MATERIALS

1. Same as for the phenol-phthalein field method except methyl orange is used in place of phenolphthalein.

Total Hardness

Dropper Bottle Titration

A determination of calcium and magnesium salts is used to establish a proportion for total ion determination. This is a titrimetric method based on a color reaction which occurs when all calcium and magnesium ions are bound up by the reagent EDTA. Hardness is a simple test to conduct, with small variations in procedure from one "kit" manufacturer to the next. The chemicals are not simple; therefore, it is practical to purchase chemicals rather than make "from scratch." The following is an example of the simplicity of the "kit" procedure for hardness determination.

PROCEDURE:

1. Pipette a 10 ml sample into a 100 ml beaker.
2. Add 5–10 drops of buffer solution (should produce a pH of 10).
3. Add 2–5 drops of indicator.
4. Slowly add the EDTA titrant drop-wise, while swirling the sample over a white background. When the red begins to fade, add the drops more slowly. The blue end point is seen best under daylight or bright "day-lite" florescent lighting.
5. Equivalents for each drop of EDTA, in terms of ppm $CaCO_3$, depend upon the brand of chemical used.

MATERIALS

1. 10 ml pipette
2. 100 ml beaker
3. Solutions (in dropper bottles: 15 drops/ml):
   a. buffer solution
   b. indicator
   c. EDTA reagent

7. Dissolved Oxygen

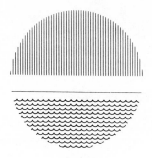

Oxygen is one of the most critical environmental factors in aquatic systems (Chap. 2). Because of the great difference between oxygen concentration in the air and in the water, water samples are easily contaminated by air contact. Special collecting techniques are necessary (App.).

The Winkler technique is the basic chemical method of dissolved oxygen determination. It is relatively accurate, but has the disadvantages of bulky glassware and short-lived chemicals that need refrigeration. It also has a rather touchy end point. However, when the Winkler test is done correctly, it is one of the best methods of oxygen determination.

Some "kit" modifications of the Winkler method have proven to be very valuable in field applications. They tend to complement the standard Winkler. The Winkler test is accurate but prone to human error. The "kit" Winkler modifications have a rather constant error that tends not to be influenced by the experimenter. The chemicals are stable and pre-measured for consistency. The "kit" test is good for establishing approximate concentrations of dissolved oxygen.

Finally, the electronic oxygen probe is probably the best method of determining oxygen concentration. Its main disadvantage is the initial expense. It must be calibrated at regular intervals by a chemical method.

Dissolved Oxygen Tests

WINKLER: AZIDE MODIFICATION

PROCEDURE:

1. Collect the water sample in a sampler (App.) that will prevent contact between the water and the air. Record the water temperature and the time of collection. The sample should be run into a 300 ml BOD bottle.
2. To the sample in the BOD bottle, using pipettes or calibrated dropper bottles, add:
   a. 2 ml of manganous sulfate solution
   b. 2 ml of alkali-iodide-azide reagent (AIA)
   These should be added well below the surface of the sample.
3. Stopper in a way that will exclude all air, and shake well. A yellow floc (a fluffy sediment that settles to the bottom) will form. Allow this floc to partially settle.
4. Shake again, and allow the floc to partially resettle.
5. Add 2 ml of concentrated sulfuric acid* (or an acid packet) to the

---

*Caution, highly corrosive.

MATERIALS
1. Water sampler
2. Thermometer
3. 300 ml BOD bottle or equivalent
4. Burette for sulfuric acid
5. 500 ml Erlenmeyer flask
6. Burette, stand, and clamp for sodium thio-sulfate titration
7. Solutions:
   a. Manganous sulfate*
   b. Alkali-iodide-azide (AIA)*
   c. Concentrated sulfuric acid or sulfamic acid packets
   d. 0.0375 N Sodium thiosulfate solution
   e. Starch solution in dropper bottle

---

* In glass-stoppered bottles with premeasured glass pipettes or burettes.

AIR CONTAMINATION OF
DISSOLVED OXYGEN (DO)

It is important to avoid air contact with water samples destined for dissolved oxygen analysis. There is much more oxygen in the air than in water. The smallest trapped air bubble will alter dissolved oxygen readings. Precautions are necessary from the time of collection to final preparation of DO test sample. When the reagents are added to the water sample, they displace some of the water, and make the container "too full." If the ground glass stopper is centered over the bottle opening, the excess fluid is forced out and the stopper is seated underwater. With a small amount of practice this procedure can be perfected, and rarely will air bubbles be trapped in the sample bottle. Because some surface water is lost, the reagents must be inserted below the water surface.

sample. Stopper and shake. The floc should dissolve. If it does not, add another 0.5 ml of acid, stopper, and shake.

6. Pour the 300 ml sample solution into a 500 ml Erlenmeyer flask.
   (Half of the 300 ml sample size may be used; if so, the results must be multiplied by 2 to give equivalent results.)

7. Fill the burette with thiosulfate solution. Free the burette of air bubbles. Note the level of the sodium thiosulfate in the burette. Titrate with sodium thiosulfate until the sample is a pale straw color. (Careful, this is a tricky end point.)

8. Add 1–2 ml of starch solution. The sample will turn blue.* If it does not, you have added too much thiosulfate and must begin again.

9. Continue titrating to the first disappearance of the blue color. This lack of color should persist when the solution is swirled. Record the new level of the thiosulfate and then calculate the difference between the two thiosulfate readings.

CALCULATIONS:

Each ml of thiosulfate is equivalent to one ppm of DO. Thus DO can be read directly from the burette at this normality of thiosulfate (0.0375) and with a 300 ml sample size.

TEST MECHANICS:

1. Manganous sulfate and AIA produce the floc which reacts with the DO.
2. When the acid is added, free iodine is released in proportional amounts to the original DO.
3. The iodine is then titrated with thiosulfate.

---

* Interference with blue color reaction at this step may also be due to old starch and/or AIA solutions. To check these solutions, a small amount of starch solution added to the AIA solution under acid conditions should produce a blue color.

TEST LIMITATIONS:

1. The interval between acidification and titration must not be longer than 45 minutes.
2. Nitrates, ferrous iron, high organic content, or suspended solids may interfere with results (*Standard Methods,* 1971: 474).

FIELD METHOD: HACH

PROCEDURE:

1. Collect the water sample in a sampler (App.) that will prevent contact between water and air. Record the water temperature and the time of collection.
2. Fill the 60 ml DO bottle with the water to be tested.
3. Add the contents of one pillow each of Dissolved Oxygen Powder I and Dissolved Oxygen Powder II. Stopper in a manner to exclude air. Shake to mix and allow the floc that is formed to settle.
4. Shake again and let the floc resettle. Add the contents of one pillow Dissolved Oxygen Powder III.
5. Stopper and shake. The floc should disappear and a yellow color will form if oxygen is present.
6. Fill the calibrated plastic measuring tube level full (5.8 ml) with the prepared sample. Pour it into the mixing bottle.
7. While swirling the sample to mix, add PAO* dropwise counting each drop, until the sample changes from yellow to colorless. The dropper must be held vertically. The parts per million (ppm) is equal to the number of drops added.

METHOD FOR INCREASED SENSITIVITY:

1, 2, 3, are the same as above.

---

*PAO solution decomposes if it is allowed to stand in sunlight.

SATURATION

The amount of gas that can be dissolved in water is not the same for all conditions. Water can contain more gas under cold, fresh, and high pressure conditions. Thus a cold trout stream near sea level will have a large amount of O_2 at saturation, while a warm, salty pool will have much less oxygen at saturation. When a reading is taken in ppm, it is useful to know what percentage of saturation the reading represents. Amounts of O_2 in ppm and equivalent amounts in % saturation at different temperatures may be determined by a nomogram (Figure 7–1, p. 68).

MATERIALS

1. Hach or other water sampler
2. 60 ml DO Bottle
3. Calibrated measuring tube (5.8 ml)
4. Mixing bottle
5. Reagents:
   a. Dissolved Oxygen I (Manganous sulfate)
   b. Dissolved Oxygen II (Alkaline-Iodide-Azide)
   c. Dissolved Oxygen III (Dry Acid)
   d. PAO (Phenylarsene oxide)

Correction Factors for Oxygen
Saturation at Various Altitudes

| Altitude | | Pressure | |
Feet	Metres	mm.	Factor
0	0	760	1.00
330	100	750	1.01
655	200	741	1.03
980	300	732	1.04
1310	400	723	1.05
1640	500	714	1.06
1970	600	705	1.08
2300	700	696	1.09
2630	800	687	1.11
2950	900	679	1.12
3280	1000	671	1.13
3610	1100	663	1.15
3940	1200	655	1.16
4270	1300	647	1.17
4600	1400	639	1.19
4930	1500	631	1.20
5250	1600	623	1.22
5580	1700	615	1.24
5910	1800	608	1.25
6240	1900	601	1.26
6560	2000	594	1.28
6900	2100	587	1.30
7220	2200	580	1.31
7550	2300	573	1.33
7880	2400	565	1.34
8200	2500	560	1.36

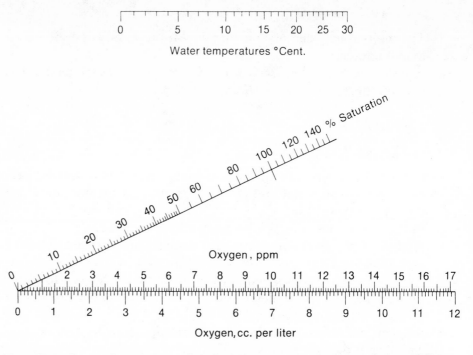

Figure 7–1 *Rawson's nomogram for obtaining oxygen-saturation values at different temperatures and at different altitudes; also for transforming oxygen values from one kind of unit to another. When a ruler, or preferably a dark-colored thread, is held so as to join an observed temperature on the upper scale with the observed dissolved-oxygen value on the lower scale, the values or units desired are read at points where the thread or ruler crosses the other scales. The associated table supplies correction values for oxygen saturation at various altitudes; for example: if 6.4 cc. per liter of oxygen is observed in a sample from a lake having an altitude of approximately 500 m. (1640 ft.), the amount of oxygen which would be present at sea level under the same circumstances is found by multiplying 6.4 by the factor 1.06, giving the product 6.8; then the percentage saturation is determined by connecting 6.8 on the lower scale with the observed temperature on top scale and noting point of intersection on middle (diagonal) scale. (Redrawn from Rawson, Spec. Pub. No. 15, Limn. Soc. Am., 1944.) (Welch, 1948: 366; reprinted with permission.)*

4. Pour off contents of the DO bottle until the level just reaches the mark on the bottle (29 ml).
5. While swirling the DO bottle to mix the sample, add PAO dropwise, counting each drop, until the sample changes from yellow to colorless. Each drop of PAO added is equal to 0.2 ppm dissolved oxygen in the sample.

TEST MECHANICS:

Similar to Winkler except that PAO is used in place of thiosulfate. PAO is much more stable and is more suitable for use in the field. (Parts of the above are courtesy of Hach Chemical Company.)

FIELD METHOD: LaMOTTE*

PROCEDURE:

1. Collect the water sample in a sampler that will prevent contact between the water and the air. Record the water temperature and the time of collection.
2. Fill the plastic sample bottle with the water to be tested.
3. Add 8 drops of manganese sulfate solution and 8 drops of alkaline potassium iodide solution to the sample. Shake to mix and allow the floc that is formed to settle.
4. Add 0.5 ml of sulfuric acid. Stopper and shake until the floc disappears.
5. Fill the flask to the 50 ml line with the water sample.
6. Fill the microburette with sodium thiosulfate solution.
7. Titrate the sample with thiosulfate until the brown color almost disappears. Add 8 drops of starch solution. The sample will turn blue. Continue titrating until the blue color disappears.

MATERIALS

1. Water sampler
2. Plastic sample bottle
3. 50 ml Erlenmeyer flask
4. Microburette
5. Droppers
6. Solutions:
   a. Manganese sulfate
   b. Alkaline potassium iodide
   c. Sulfuric acid
   d. Starch solution
   e. Sodium thiosulfate

---

*Courtesy of LaMotte Chemical Company.

8. Each major division of the microburette equals 0.2 ppm. (Each smaller division equals 0.04 ppm.)

Membrane Electrode Method

Accurate oxygen measurement through the use of an electronic sensor is ideal, considering the rather drawn out chemical procedures. However, the limitations and technical problems of oxygen probes have often, in past years, proven to be more difficult than the chemical methods they were designed to replace. Add to this the substantial outlay for such an instrument ($400–$700 + accessories), and the probe method loses much of its attraction.

Many of the past problems have been associated with electrodes exposed to the medium under investigation. Such exposed elements are very susceptible to contamination and interference. Since the development of the membrane covered electrodes, many of these objections have been overcome, and some rather reliable units are now available.

While different specific instructions are included with the instrument from each manufacturer, certain similarities of operation do exist. The two basic types are polarographic and galvanic. The main difference between the two is that the galvanic reaction is polarized by an outside source of electricity, while the polarographic is spontaneous. In both systems, the chemical reaction, taking place across the anode and cathode inside the measuring cell, "consumes" oxygen. The dissolved oxygen level, on the inside of the cell membrane after equilibration, is zero. The rate of flow of oxygen, through the membrane from the outside of the cell, is proportional to amounts of dissolved oxygen in the water being measured.

The water next to the outer surface of the membrane will become depleted of oxygen as it flows into the probe's measuring cell. There must be a circulation of water in the vicinity of the membrane. If stirring or other agitation is not done, the loss of accuracy is substantial. Stirrers increase the effective cost of the instrument but, realistically, must be considered for most applications. Agitating the probe by sloshing it up and down while hanging over the side of the boat usually results in repair bills that could have been used for the purchase of a stirrer.

We have found dramatic differences in quality and service of dissolved oxygen probes, even at equivalent prices. This seems to be an area where comparing equipment is justified. Most manufacturers will loan equipment or provide demonstrations prior to purchase.

8. Biochemical Oxygen Demand (BOD)

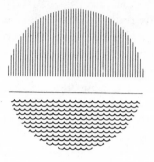

The effects of materials that will soon decompose may not be apparent at the time of sampling. However, when decomposition does begin, there is a rapid drop in dissolved oxygen that is detrimental to the community. When plants or animals die, the decomposers in the community, bacteria and fungi, go to work to break down the organic materials involved. Respiration of the bacteria and fungi demands oxygen. At normal population turnover rates, the oxygen demand is not great and oxygen concentrations are adequate for survival of the remaining aquatic community. However, when there are large "kills" of organisms or when oxygen-demanding pollutants are added to waters, there is greater possibility for the water to drop to low oxygen levels.

The problem boils down to one of prediction. In a BOD test, the potential loss of oxygen due to decomposition (oxidation) is measured. Probably, the conditions of the waters from which the sample was taken will produce less oxygen drop than that of laboratory conditions. One of the laboratory conditions is total darkness, which probably will not be encountered in the stream/lake environment. But under certain conditions in a natural situation, there may be total darkness for a time equivalent to the time of the laboratory test. The upshot of all this is that there is no direct applicability of laboratory tests to natural environments. The BOD test is an index to the quality of the water under laboratory conditions. What happens to the water in nature is subject to many variables including depth, water clarity, currents, substrate, and light intensity. Although the BOD test is conducted under artificial conditions, it gives an important indication of the predisposition of an aquatic situation to develop oxygen deficiencies or other related problems. It is important not to equate inaccuracy with lack of importance or significance. In some situations the BOD test, with all of its difficulties, is the only way of evaluating potential environmental problems.

BOD Test

BOD measures the tendency of elements within a water sample to consume oxygen. The water is tested for dissolved oxygen, then incubated and tested again. The measured drop in oxygen indicates possible similar oxygen-depletions in some natural situations. It is important to avoid making direct generalizations from laboratory BOD to natural situations. Conditions vary between laboratory and aquatic environments, as well as from one environment to the next.

MATERIALS

1. Water sampler
2. Two 300 ml BOD bottles
3. Incubator or equivalent conditions
4. Materials for dissolved oxygen determination

PROCEDURE:

1. Collect the water sample in a sampler that will prevent contact between the water and the air. Record the water temperature and the time of collection. The sample should be run into two 300 ml BOD bottles. Put them in a cool place out of direct sunlight until they are returned to the laboratory.
2. Determine the dissolved oxygen concentration (DO) in one of the BOD bottles (Chap. 7). The second BOD bottle will be tested later.
3. Record the DO. To avoid confusion with other samples, record the date, the time of collection, and the number of the second (untested) BOD sample. BOD bottles usually come with serial numbers painted on each bottle.
4. Incubate the second BOD bottle in a dark place at 20°C ($\pm 1°$).
5. At the end of a five day period, measure the DO in the second sample and subtract it from the original measurement.
6. Results are expressed in ppm of BOD.

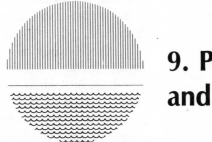

9. Phosphate and Nitrate

Survey of Nutrient Salts Determination

According to the law of the minimum (Chap. 1), one or, at the most, a few elements are going to control population growth. The nutrients that usually limit aquatic populations are phosphorus and nitrogen compounds.

The techniques in *Standard Methods* (1971) for the determination of phosphate and nitrate are difficult and expensive. In most teaching situations, field "kit" determinations of these nutrients are more practical. For purposes of calibration, an occasional duplicate sample should be run by a commercial testing laboratory. The names and addresses of such laboratories can be obtained from local branches of the U.S. Soil Conservation Service.

Nitrogen gas (N_2) is abundant in the atmosphere, but cannot be used by most plants. Biologically available forms of nitrogen are ammonia gas dissolved in water, nitrate, and nitrite. Tests for available nitrogen normally measure nitrate and nitrite only, because these forms represent total available nitrogen under most conditions, and because the nitrate and nitrite tests are less difficult than the ammonia test. However, under some conditions it is valuable to have determinations of ammonia.

Phosphate available for plant growth commonly occurs in two forms: metaphosphate and the more simply structured orthophosphate.

It is important to make all phosphate and nitrate/nitrite determinations as soon as possible after sample collection. As organic material in the water begins to break down, some of the more complex, "bound" forms of phosphorus and nitrogen are simplified by decomposition, and increase the levels of phosphate and nitrate/nitrite.

Hach Chemical Company uses a simplification of the *Standard Method's* determination. Indicator reagents produce color reactions proportional to the amounts of nitrate/nitrite or phosphate in the sample. Intensity of color is measured by the photocell of a colorimeter. A color filter is provided to exaggerate the color response. Such colorimeter determinations are the most accurate of the field methods. They do have initial high expense, ranging from professional laboratory equipment ($500–$4,000) to less expensive, barely adequate units ($75–$200).

Another method of nutrient determination uses color standards. Solutions of colored indicators are made up using exact amounts of nitrogen or phosphorus. The color of the treated sample is compared to a row of such standards. Instructions for making standards are included in *Standard Methods* (1971). Often, for the kinds of approximations inherent in field conditions, a visual comparison method using permanent standards, such as that of the LaMotte Chemical Company, will serve. In the LaMotte test, the standards are incorporated into a color comparator. The sample is moved from one slot to another, until the closest color match is obtained. The value for phosphate or nitrate is then read from the comparator.

10. Biological Tests

Under the most carefully controlled conditions, a laboratory animal will do just as it pleases. If this is true under laboratory conditions, then it must be doubly true in field situations where there are no controls over environmental conditions. The basic problem in most biological field situations is the determination of a representative sample. Biological collecting seeks to determine what kind of animals there are, how many there are, and under what conditions they are present.

It is difficult to determine the point at which a sample is representative of the population. Increasing probability of sample validity is gained by conducting a series of tests and comparing variations between them. If a series of tests are made and variations between them are compared, an estimate can be obtained of how well the sample represents the natural population. An adequate sample series at one place, or under one set of conditions, may not be adequate under other conditions. Animals may travel in schools, or they may aggregate as a function of cold or other factors. Depending upon the time of year, they may reside at different depths or even separate by sex. Environmental factors controlling such movements may change. For example, at one time of the year temperature may control movement, while at another time food supply might control movement. A single sample may be taken in the middle of an aggregation, or in the space between two aggregations. If it is assumed that either of the samples taken are representative of the population, the estimate will be too high in the first case and too low in the second case.

Thus sampling does have inherent errors. The behavior of the creatures being collected (their distribution, activity, ease of capture, and size distribution) may result in their abundance being under or overestimated. Quantitative statements should not be made until repeated collections verify counts. Each collecting technique has its own bias which adds to possible error.

Sampling is necessary and valuable. Even though the physical (abiotic) aspects of the environment are known, the relationships between them and the biological agents (biotic) must also be known. A description of the biotic nature of an environment — the biological community — can impart a great deal of information. The animals that are observed are adapted for a particular range of conditions. The variation of conditions over time, the productivity, and the general stability of an environment can often be determined through a biological assessment. Some plants and animals are used as "indicator organisms" because they are so closely associated with a particular range of conditions.

Sampling should always be done with consideration for the environment and for others that may follow. Littering and destroying delicate vegetation are obviously detrimental to environmental quality. More subtle, but often just as injurious, are inconsiderate actions such as stream bed disturbances (related to the "put the rock back the way it was" rule of tidepool work) and collection of specimens. It is easy to deplete a stream of large fish or other vertebrates with efficient collecting equipment, particularly if the site is visited regularly by class trips. A seashore or delicate habitat can be devastated by an uninstructed class field trip. Ignorance in handling fishes or the "let's start a collection" syndrome may also spoil a habitat for use by others.

Certain communities are considered valuable or pleasing to man and efforts are made to maintain those communities. When conditions begin to change, modifying the community in an undesirable direction, shifts in the relative numbers of members of the biological community can be observed (sometimes even when physico-chemical tests do not reveal a change). Such changes will be associated with the appearance of members of communities adapted to less desirable conditions. An example might be a "clean river" community including trout, large aquatic insects, small-mouth bass, and minnows. The appearance of fly larvae, carp, blue green algae, or midge larvae serves as a warning that conditions might be deteriorating.

Increasing human population is making it necessary to manage resources wisely in order to avoid increasing environmental deterioration. Multiple use of resources represents a move toward environmental management. A river, for example, can be used for recreation, industrial, domestic, and esthetic purposes. Each use has to be managed with concern for the other uses. If one use overexploits the resource, the potential for other uses will be decreased. For example, coliform bacteria tests (an indicator of untreated domestic sewage) measure domestic use of water resources. If coliform levels are high, the water may not be suitable for recreation and other uses, and its total resource value will be impaired.

Use of Identification Keys

An identification key is based on a choice, which then leads to another choice, then to another, and so on, until finally all possibilities are eliminated except a single identification. All living organisms are named, using a two word ("binomial") system. The genus is the first word, and the species is the second word. The genus designates a group of closely related animals and is capitalized; the species is particular to one animal and is not capitalized. Both words are italicized. For example, the cats are of the genus *Felis* and some members of the cat group are: *Felis domestica* (housecat), *Felis leo* (lion), and *Felis tigris* (tiger).

It is valuable for students who have never used a key to construct one, identifying miscellaneous items of hardware. The following example of a key classifies screws and nails. It adds to the fun of the exercise to name the species that are keyed out.

1a   Shank smooth or with concentric ridges.   **Nail**   *Go to 2*
1b   Shank with spiral sharp ridge (threads).   **Screw**   *Go to 5*

2a   Nail with slight swelling at anterior end.   **Finishing nail,** Genus: *Finishia*   *Go to 3*
2b   Nail with flat, round plate at anterior end.   *Go to 4*

3a   Nail less than 10 cm long.   **Lesser finishing nail,** *Finishia minutia*
3b   Nail more than 10 cm long.   **Greater finishing nail,** *Finishia bigone*

4a   Nail with smooth shank.   **Penny nail,** Genus: *Pennia*
(Several species in this genus: *Pennia teni, Pennia sixi,* etc. Depends on length and weight)
4b   Nail with concentric ridges.   **Dry wall nail,** *Drywallia staystucki*

5a   Shank tapered.   **Wood fastening screw** or **Sheet metal screw,** Genus: *Threadsgrippita*   *Go to etc.*

5b Shank cylindrical. **Machine screw** or **bolt,** Genus: *Needsanutta
    Go to etc.*

5c Shank tapered but large and partially threaded, head square or hex-
    agonal (to be turned with a wrench). **Lag screw,** Genus: *Hold-
    salotta   Go to etc.*

There is nothing wrong (you are not "cheating") with looking at
the pictures, especially to get an idea of the general characteristics of a
group. If the organism in question is located in a drawing, check the key
to verify the identification. Soon you will get a feeling for the characteristics of certain groups.

11. Plankton

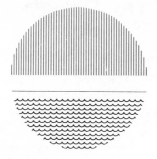

The objectives of a plankton study are to determine what species of plankters (free-floating, microscopic organisms) are in the water, and in what proportions they exist. Another measurement, plankton density or creatures per cubic meter, also gives valuable information. It provides an indication of the productivity of an environment, and may indicate distributional patterns by allowing density comparisons of one area to another. A plankton net (Figure 11–1) pulled through the water will collect most species present. But, in order to get proportional samples, the net must strain enough water to offset the effects of plankton clumping. Certain species will predominate in some areas and be absent from others. If the net is drawn through a clump or a sparse area, that particular species will be over or under-represented, compared to its occurrence

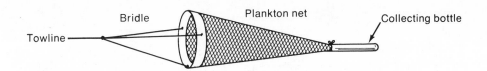

Figure 11-1 Plankton net showing towline and collecting bottle.

in the water as a whole. For a density determination, the amount of water that passes through the net must be estimated.

There are many kinds of plankton collection techniques which measure the exact amount of water sampled so that the number of organisms in a cubic meter can be calculated. The water may be measured by trapping a measured volume of water and then pouring it through a net (Kemmerer method). Another technique uses a calibrated, miniature propeller mounted in the opening of a net. There are other more complex methods as well, involving pumps and large traps (Welch, 1948).

Only two plankton sampling methods are relatively inexpensive and both have some drawbacks. In the towed net method, the amount of water really passing through the mesh is difficult to measure. The Kemmerer method takes an exact size sample, but the volume of the sample is so small that the proportions of animals in it may not represent the proportions in the total community. These problems might be more serious if the entire plankton sampling procedure were not approximate. Under natural conditions, plankters clump, disperse, migrate both vertically and horizontally, and even hide in the mud. They do these things in response to a variety of stimuli, including light, temperature, and food supply. The nature of a particular plankton sample will depend upon how the sampling device was moved with respect to the distribution of plankton. A sample should always be considered as an approximation of what is really in the water. Streams are much easier to sample than still water. Their tumbling action distributes the plankton rather evenly, and makes a given sample more representative.

Plankton Sampling: Field Techniques

Before any plankton-sampling procedure, the net should be checked and washed or repaired if necessary. To avoid confusion during collection, samples should be kept in a rack and labeled to indicate collecting stations. Notes, including proper collection data (App.), should be made during each plankton-collecting run.

HORIZONTAL TOW METHOD

This technique is capable of sampling extensive amounts of water by prolonged tows. Surface waters are easily sampled, and mid-depths may also be sampled by controlling boat speed, weighting the front of the net, and calculating the depth.*

Horizontally towed nets collect large samples of plankton. It is difficult to tell how much water was strained to yield the sample, in order to calculate the original plankton density. The amount of water that flows through the net hoop can be calculated, but the resistance of the net causes some of the water to be pushed to the sides of the net opening. This resistance, called the "net factor," is a function of tow speed and

---

*
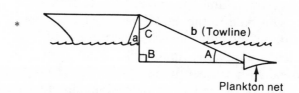
Plankton net

Angle B is 90°. Angle C can be measured from the boat with an inclinometer. Angle $A = 90° - C$. Distance b is known (the amount of line let out with the plankton net). Depth a may be found by the following relationship: $\sin A = a/b$, $a = b (\sin A)$.

mesh size. The net factor changes with these two variables and is difficult to compute.

Another method of computing approximate density is to use the Kemmerer method as a standard. If no Kemmerer sampler is available, any hand-held container will serve but, of course, will probably be restricted to surface water use. Repeated Kemmerer samples that agree closely can be used to determine plankton density. For example, if the density of a plankter is determined by the Kemmerer method to be $20/m^3$ and a horizontal tow yields 100 of the same species, then the net of the horizontal tow strained approximately $100/20 = 5\ m^3$ of water. Remember that this method is approximate and must be used with large, rather non-motile forms of plankton. Also, the tow speed and mesh size must be constant for each density calibration. This determination should be checked frequently, using different species to confirm calibration values.

PROCEDURE:

1. Bring boat to towing speed (1–3 miles/hour). Speed must be the same for every tow if density estimates are being made. Lower the net into water, bottle first, to float out air bubbles.
2. Play out line as rapidly as possible while still keeping net in surface waters.
3. Tie off the line at a premeasured distance (50 feet or so). Tow for a predetermined period of time (1 to 5 minutes depending on plankton density).
4. At the end of the tow period, stop boat and pull in plankton net. Record time of tow, and other collection data (App.).
5. Unscrew or unfasten bottle. Wash net by drawing through the water several times with net bottle removed and replace bottle for next tow. Plankton may be maintained in collecting bottles or transferred to specimen bottles. Transfer bottle to rack.

MATERIALS

1. Phytoplankton net No. 20 silk bolting cloth (173 meshes per inch)
2. Towline
3. Collecting bottles in rack
4. Formalin/glycerin solution
5. Boat and motor or equivalent
6. Thermometer
7. Water sampler or equivalent

Vertical Tow Method

Vertical distribution of plankton can be sampled by a simple net method. By lowering a net to a 5 foot depth and then drawing it up, only plankton at 5 feet or less are taken. Several collections should be taken at this depth. The next vertical tow is made at a depth of 10 feet and only plankton at 10 feet or less are taken. The tows of 5 and 10 feet depths can then be compared. If species are seen in the 10 foot deep tow that were not in the 5 foot deep tow, then those plankton may have been stratified in the 5–10 foot layer. By continuing this procedure, vertical stratification of plankton can be determined. This is particularly important in establishing relationships of plankton to the thermocline (Chap. 2).

PROCEDURE:

1. Lower net to desired depth using measurements marked on line in feet or meters.
2. Haul net vertically. Remove bottle and transfer to rack. Record collection data (App.).
3. Wash net and replace net bottle.
4. Repeat vertical tow at next depth increment.

Kemmerer Sampler

In this technique an exact volume of water is sampled, and then poured through a net. The plankton left in the net represents density for an exact volume, such as one liter. Density can be converted to yield plankters per cubic meter (m^3), the conventional unit of plankton density, by multiplying the count for one liter by 1000. One advantage of this method is that different depths of water can be sampled. Also, by comparing counts from net tows (where the volume is not known) to

Kemmerer counts (where a volume is known), a calibration of the tow method is possible.

PROCEDURE:

1. Open sampler and lock in position.
2. Lower sampler into water to desired depth, using measurements marked on line in feet or meters.
3. With sampler at desired depth, release messenger, close sampler, and haul sampler up.
4. Have a partner hold plankton net outboard of boat, with net-opening in a convenient position for step 5.
5. Hold sampler over the opening of the net. Open the sampler, and allow the water sample to wash through the net.
6. Unscrew or unfasten bottle. Transfer bottle to rack. Wash net and replace net bottle. Record collection data (App.).
7. Repeat at next depth increment.

"SPINNING ROD"

PROCEDURE:

Situations may arise in which time, location, or other reasons prevent collection of plankton by conventional methods. A collection might often be valuable in these situations. A way of making tows under such conditions is to construct a small, simple net. A net made from a nylon stocking, with a small hoop (4 to 6 inches) made from a coat hanger and a bridle of nylon line, serves as a miniature, portable plankton net. It can be cast considerable distances using an inexpensive spinning outfit and it can be quickly retrieved. This method is a quick way of making a qualitative plankton survey.

Procedures for Plankton Work

1. *Recovery of total plankters collected:* When a tow is brought to the boat, there are often many plankters on the net material. To work these specimens into the bottle, use the water that is already in the net material. Bunch the net together at the top, encircle it with thumb and fingers, and gently slide your hand toward the bottle. This procedure "milks" the water and associated plankters from the net towards the bottle. Sometimes it is helpful to pour a small amount of water from the bottle (through the adjacent netting) in advance of this procedure so that the bottle is not too full.

2. *Washing net:* After each tow, the net should be washed by drawing it through the water several times with the bottle removed.

3. *Handling:* Most plankton are delicate. When they are crowded into a collecting bottle, and later into specimen bottles, the larger forms thrash about and damage smaller forms. It is advisable to preserve collections as soon as possible to minimize this effect. If preservation is to be done, it should be done in the field. For study of living specimens, uncrowded samples in thermos bottles do well for several hours. For later keying, which often requires living specimens, a subsample is valuable.

4. *Preservation:* Preservative should be 4% formalin measured by volume, with a few drops of glycerin added per 100 ml. The glycerin helps maintain flexibility of body parts of the preserved organisms. For long-term storage, formalin should be buffered (Humason, 1962: 14).

5. *Specimen deterioration:* Many species of plankton deteriorate rapidly, even when preserved. For best results, count as soon as possible (a few hours) after collection.

6. *Sub-sampling:* When a sub-sample is taken from the specimen bottle, the sample bottle should be swirled to temporarily suspend the plankters. This allows the sub-sample to be representative of the sample.

7. *Pipetting:* When a 1 ml sub-sample is taken for study in the Sedgwick-Rafter Counting Cell (Figure 11–2), care should be taken that the plankters are not damaged by being forced through the small orifice of a pipette. One way of avoiding such damage to the plankton specimens is to measure 1 ml of water into a small dish, then take the water up into an eyedropper with a large orifice. The eyedropper is then marked at the 1 ml line and used in place of a pipette for transfers to the Sedgwick-Rafter Cell.

8. *Ocular micrometers:* Ocular micrometers (calibrated grids placed in the eyepiece of the microscope) are available from any biological supply house. However, they must be calibrated with a stage micrometer (a measuring device placed on the stage of the microscope). For example, the Whipple ocular micrometer is designed to frame one square millimeter (mm^2) of the field of view on the microscope slide. The stage micrometer (in this case, anything measuring 1 mm^2) is set on the slide, and the microscope is adjusted until a 1 mm line on the ocular micrometer matches a 1 mm line on the stage micrometer. Then the stage micrometer is removed. All of the positions of zoom lens, objectives, and oculars necessary to achieve this calibration should be recorded, and repeated for any subsequent sessions in which such measurements must be made.

For Sedgwick-Rafter work random counts may be made, based on the dimensions of the counting cell ($50 \times 20 \times 1$ mm $= 1000$ mm^3 or 1 cc). The Whipple micrometer is 1 square mm, and it outlines 1 cubic mm when it is superimposed on the counting cell. Then random counts of several cubic mm can be used to estimate the population of the entire counting cell. For example, 10 random counts are made by counting all organisms within the grid of the Whipple micrometer. The total volume counted is 10 mm³ which is $10/1000 = 1/100$ of the entire volume of the cell. For a projection to the total count of the cell, multiply results of the 10 counts by 100. Projected counts should be compared to reliable estimates of the total cell population to determine if the random counts are sufficient in number.

9. *Plankton nets* are produced in various mesh sizes. To sample the small phytoplankton (including diatoms, desmids, etc.), a small number 20 mesh net is commonly used. To sample larger plankters (copepods, cladocerans, etc.), larger mesh sizes are more efficient.

Plankton Sampling: Laboratory Techniques

PROCEDURE:

> MATERIALS
> 1. Microscope with micrometer or mechanical stage
> 2. Plankton key
> 3. Sedgwick-Rafter Counting Cell with cover slip
> 4. 1.0 ml calibrated eyedropper

1. Dilute specimen concentration with water to 100 ml. If sample is to be preserved, include in the dilution water 4 ml of 100% formalin (100% formalin = 40% formaldehyde) and a few drops of glycerin. For best specimen condition, preservation should be done in the field.
2. Lay a cover slip diagonally across the chamber of a Sedgwick-Rafter Counting Cell (Figure 11–2).
3. Gently swirl the sample to suspend the specimens and extract 1.0 ml from the stirred plankton.
4. Apply the dropper into one of the exposed corners of the counting cell, and slowly release the contents into the cell. The cover slip should slowly swing into alignment with the cell by surface attrac-

tion. The cover slip should need only a slight nudge for final alignment, when the full ml is placed in the cell.

5. Several methods may be employed in counting plankton:

   a. Scan counting cell with dissecting scope to count large species first. Then carefully examine with compound microscope for smaller species (steps b and c).

   b. "Spot check" with compound scope: stop at random locations and count all plankters on calibrated grid, such as an ocular micrometer that is a known fraction of the cell (see procedures for plankton work). This is a good method if no mechanical stage is available.

   c. Compound scope, careful scan (requires mechanical stage): adjust the microscope focus for most comfortable viewing. Establish number of rows necessary to cover entire counting chamber. Start across on first row, keeping tally ($\cancel{||||}$) of each species on a tally sheet. Count all rows, or a sample of rows (if there is agreement between rows). Add up tallies for each species, or take an average of tallies for sample rows and multiply by the total number of rows to obtain actual or projected number of plankters in the cell (cell count). It is easy to break the cell cover slip or damage the optics when using a high-power objective with the Sedgwick-Rafter Counting Cell.

6. Multiply cell count by 100 to obtain projected number taken in net haul. The cell is 1/100 of the volume of the original sample.

7. Divide projected number from net haul by number of m^3 that the net strained to obtain number of plankters/m^3 (see calibration by Kemmerer method to determine plankters/m^3).

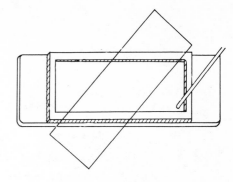

Figure 11–2 Sedgwick-Rafter Counting Cell.

Plankton Identification Key

It is not always easy to distinguish one-celled plants from one-celled animals. Practice and checking against pictures is the best way to get a sense of which is which. It should be comforting to a person unfamiliar with identification of these creatures, that many single-celled organisms are claimed by both botanists ("they are plants because they have chlorophyll") and zoologists ("they are animals because they can live without chlorophyll, by eating other creatures"). The larger part of almost any freshwater plankton community can be identified, at least to major group, by the following key. Although the key has been deliberately kept simple, the wide distributional pattern of freshwater plankton assures that many common species will be identifiable. It is hoped that with the information obtained from this key, the reader will turn to an authoritative plankton reference, such as Pennak (1953) or Ward and Whipple (1966). This key is designed for freshwater. Scientific names are used where no convenient common name is available. General references are provided in the appendix. Local Audubon groups, Sierra Club chapters, or other nature-oriented groups should be consulted for regional guides.

1a Plankter is an animal. Active, usually not green or otherwise strongly pigmented (although gut may be green from feeding on plants). Cilia or flagella may be used for locomotion. **Zooplankton** *Go to 2*

1b Plankter is a plant. Almost always strongly pigmented (may be bright green, yellow, orange-red, orange, yellow-brown, or dark blue-green). If appendages, they are visible only under high magnification. **Phytoplankton** *Go to 10*

2a Animal is a single cell. **Protozoa** *Go to 3*
2b Animal has more than one cell. *Go to 4*

3a Body "shapeless," resembling animated fluid-filled bag. **Amoeba** (Figure 1)

3b Body encased or centrally organized with long sticky processes radiating out in starburst pattern. **Heliozoans** and relatives (Figures 2–5)

3c Body totally encased in shell or test, having appearance of a stone wall or rough mosaic. **Difflugia** and relatives (Figures 6–8)

Figure 1   Amoeba

Figure 2   Nuclearia

Figure 3   Actinosphaerium

Figure 4   Actinophrys

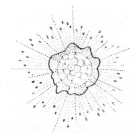

Figure 5   Vampyrella

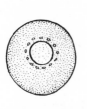

Figure 6   Arcella

Figure 7   Difflugia acuminata

Figure 8   Difflugia corona

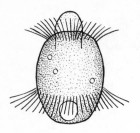

Figure 9   Didinium

3d Cell covered totally, or at least in the area near mouth, by cilia. The cilia set up currents which stir up water in immediate vicinity of the cilia (but avoid confusion with rotifers—5a). **Ciliates** (Figures 9–14)

4a Multicelled structure radially organized (circular or tube-like body structure). **Coelenterates** (Figures 15–17)

4b Multicelled structure bilaterally organized (similar right and left side of body). *Go to 5*

5a Microscopic, common, aquatic animal with rings of cilia at anterior of body. When observed on microscope slide, anterior of living, feeding animal accompanied by violent disturbances, caused by currents set up by cilia, and by body motions. Body is divided into anterior, midsection, and tail. Tail is usually forked, and may have hooks or gland which produces a cement for temporary attachment. **Rotifers** (Figures 18–21)

5b Macroscopic. Animal clearly segmented, with outer surface of the body hardened and jointed. Legs and mouth parts jointed. *Go to 6*

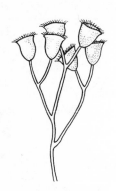

Figure 10   Epistylis

Figure 11   Paramecium

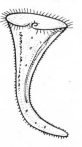

Figure 12   Stentor

Figure 13   Tintinnidium

Figure 14   Vorticella

Figure 15 *Hydra*

Figure 16 *Hydra*

Figure 17 *Freshwater jellyfish* (*Petasidae*)

Figure 18 *Asplanchna*

Figure 19 *Keratella*

Figure 20 *Philodina*

Figure 21 *Polyarthra*

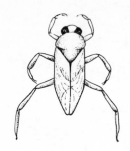

Figure 22   Back swimmer (*Notonectidae*)

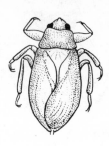

Figure 23   Giant water bug (*Belostomatidae*)

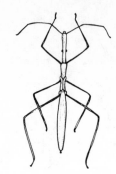

Figure 24   Marsh treader (*Hydrometridae*)

Figure 25   Water boatman (*Corixidae*)

Figure 26   Water strider (*Gerridae*)

Figure 27   Adult midge (*Tendipedidae*)

6a   Animal with three pairs of legs, body divided into head, thorax, and abdomen.   **Insects** (Figures 22–31)
(Many insects found in freshwater plankton are in immature stages which may not have legs at all.)   **Midge and mosquito larvae** (Figures 28–31)

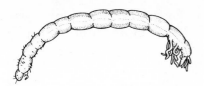

Figure 28 *Midge larva (Tendipedidae)*

Figure 29 *Midge larva (Tendipedidae)*

Figure 30 *Phantom midge larva, Chaoborus (Culicidae)*

6b Animal with more or fewer than three pairs of legs, forked appendages, and two pairs of antennae. (Some individuals may be as small as a few mm in length.) **Crustacea** *Go to 7*

7a Animal enclosed by two clam-like shells, yet still capable of rapid and sustained swimming. *Go to 9*

7b Animal with appendages easily visible. *Go to 8*

8a Trunk of body roundish in shape (but may be modified). Pair of finely branched appendages extending laterally from just below head region. Animal uses appendages to feed and to maintain position in water column. Swims by making a series of jerky, upward motions, then pauses, while it slowly sinks until the cycle is repeated. **Cladocerans** (water fleas) (Figures 32–33)

Figure 31 *Mosquito larva, Culex (Culicidae)*

Figure 32 *Bosmina*

Figure 33 *Daphnia*

8b   Animal swims gracefully, dorsal side down, with undulating series of appendages in abdominal region.   **Fairy shrimp** or **brine shrimp** (order: Anostraca) (Figure 34)

male   *female*

Figure 34   Fairy shrimp

8c   Animal with T-shaped silhouette. Antennae are long and give a "Texas Long Horn" impression. Head is anterior to a series of abdominal segments of decreasing size, forming body taper toward tail region which has two small, paired, terminal appendages. Active swimmers. Larval stages look superficially like mites.   **Copepods** (Figures 35–37)

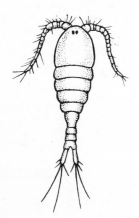

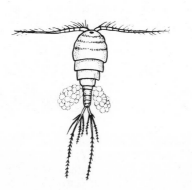

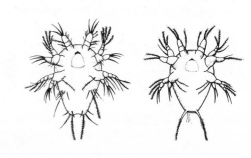

Figure 35   Copepod, Cyclops   *Figure 36   Copepod—female with eggs*   *Figure 37   Copepod larvae*

9a Head of animal near or at anterior margin of body, only partially enclosed. Head, beak shaped. May grow to ¹/₂ inch or so in length. **Clam shrimp** (order: Conchostraca) (Figure 38)

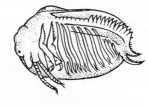

Figure 38   Clam shrimp

9b Body entirely enclosed by shells. Small size to ¹/₁₆ of inch in length. **Seed shrimp** (order: Ostracoda) (Figure 39)

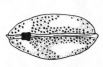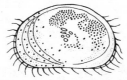

Figure 39   Seed shrimp

10a Phytoplankton that are passive. If motion is observed, it is slow and not obvious at first observation.   *Go to 11*

10b Active, single cell or cell in globe or nearly globe-shaped colony. Each cell with one or more long, whiplike flagella. The action of the flagellum may be seen before the structure itself is visible. In some forms it may act as a long tongue, used to pull in food materials to the mouth.   *Go to 13*

Figure 40   Asterionella

11a   Single cells, or combination of single cells, often showing complex patterns of texture and color. Geometric or symmetrical outlines. *Go to 12*

11b   Cells in filaments. Solitary, in groups, or in irregularly profiled colonies. May or may not have bristles.   *Go to 15*

12a   Single cell, with complex patterns of grooves over surface. Usually rod shaped, or round. Often occur in chains or circular arrangement of a few to many individuals.   **Diatoms** (Bacillariophyceae) (Figures 40–50)

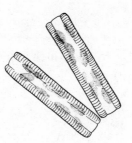

Figure 41   Cyclotella   *Figure 42   Cymbella*   *Figure 43   Diatoma*   *Figure 44   Fragilaria*   *Figure 45   Gomphonema*

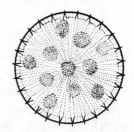

Figure 46   Melosira   *Figure 47   Navicula*   *Figure 48   Nitzschia*   *Figure 49   Stephanodiscus*   *Figure 50   Synedra*

12b Single cells, almost always solitary. Usually with one half of the cell a symmetrical copy of the other half. Cell profiles range from simple rod shape through quarter-moon shape to complex maltese-cross patterns. **Desmids** (Desmidaceae) (Figures 51–53)

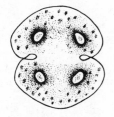

Figure 51 Cosmarium

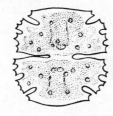

Figure 52 Closterium

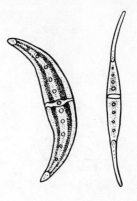

. *Figure 53 Micrasterias*

13a Single cell covered with less than 15 or so plates. Usually gold or brown in color. Flagella located in groove around midsection. Body appears to be brittle, may fragment if subjected to rough handling. Usually when present, are in large numbers, often the group responsible for yellow, brown, or red plankton "blooms." This group includes fluorescent forms and the marine organism responsible for the red tide (*Gonyaulax*). **Dinoflagellates** (Figures 54–56)

13b Single cell or colony of cells in various modifications of "tadpole" (single cell, with single or double flagellum) configuration (plants that are also called animals by zoologists). *Go to 14*

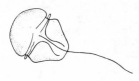

Figure 54 Gymnodinium

Figure 55 Gonyaulax

Figure 56 Ceratium

14a   Cells in actively moving colony of 4 to many individuals. Color usually bright green, but may be dull green.   **Volvox family** (Volvocaceae) (Figures 57–60)

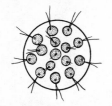

Figure 57   *Eudorina*

Figure 58   *Gonium*

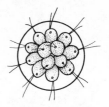

Figure 59   *Pandorina*

Figure 60   *Volvox*

14b   Isolated tadpole configuration cells. May be easily visible under the microscope (*Euglena*) or may appear as rapidly darting, small green dots, such as *Chlamydomonas* (used for algae cookies in the space programs). Often responsible for green blooms. **Motile green algae** (Chlorophyta) (Figures 61–63)

Figure 61   *Euglena*

Figure 62   *Chlamydomonas*

Figure 63   *Phacus*

15a Cells in filaments, or fragments of filaments. **Filamentous, blue-green algae** (Cyanophyta) (Figures 64–66) **Filamentous, green algae** (Chlorophyta) (Figures 67–69)

15b Solitary cells, groups of bunched cells, or colonies of cells. **Non motile, colonial, green algae** (Chlorophyta) (Figures 70–72). (Other green motile colonies are treated in 13b.)

Figure 64   *Anabaena*

Figure 65   *Aphanizomenon*

Figure 66   *Oscillatoria*

Figure 67   *Chaetophora*

Figure 68   *Spirogyra*

Figure 69   *Ulothrix*

Figure 70   *Crucigenia*

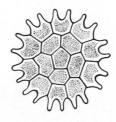

Figure 71   *Pediastrum*

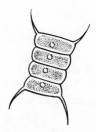

Figure 72   *Scenedesmus*

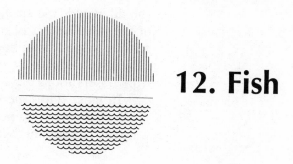

12. Fish

The fish population of an aquatic environment represents one of the most stable elements of a community. Compared to most other common aquatic forms, they are long lived and represent a high trophic level. Abundance of fish populations, their health, and the species composition of fish communities may be valuable information for an aquatic study.

Collecting Methods

Fish are difficult to collect. Schooling habits may vary between species, and even within one species from one time to the next. Fish are able to see or sense nets or other collection devices and move away. Their ability to escape may vary with turbidity of the water, temperature, bottom type, and the nature of the aquatic environment. Because of these factors, fish surveys should be considered qualitative in nature until enough collecting is done to verify quantitative information.

Fish data entered on a standard field note page or other data sheet should include the species name, size (standard length is snout tip to base of tail, total length is snout tip to tip of tail), and general condition, including sexual condition (gravid, or ovaries with eggs), parasites, and subjective weight (fat or emaciated). Much information can be gained from observations of young, spawning activity, movements, and feeding.

In most states, permission is necessary to collect fish. Usually this involves a collecting permit issued by the state. In special cases, local wardens can authorize a single collection. Even when a state permit is

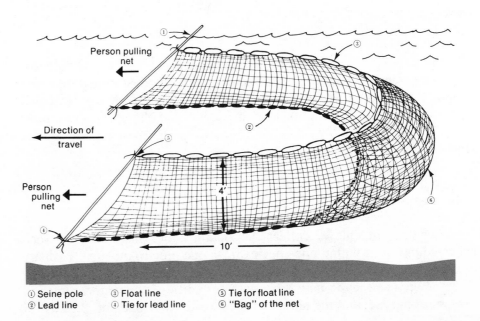

Figure 12-1 Seine operation showing 1) seine pole, 2) lead line, 3) float line, 4) tie for lead line, 5) tie for float line, 6) "bag" of the net.

① Seine pole   ③ Float line   ⑤ Tie for float line
② Lead line   ④ Tie for lead line   ⑥ "Bag" of the net

held, it is wise to notify local fish and game authorities. Some methods, such as gill netting and chemical collection, usually require a state permit, special state permission, and permission of the local warden.

Techniques for fish collection range from net methods (seines, trapping nets, gill nets, and trawls) to electrofishing, chemical methods, and hook and line. The most practical fish collection device for the biology teacher is the seine. It is a length of netting, usually ¼ inch mesh size, with a series of lead weights along the bottom, and a series of floats along the top (Figure 12–1). Four-foot lengths of netting are sold in bait shops as minnow seines and in most states are legal, as long as only "trash fish" (mostly members of the family Cyprinidae) or unprotected, non-game species are taken. Larger seines, 10 to 50 feet or more, can be used but are expensive and require a permit. Small seines are effective in small streams and closed-in areas of lakes, ponds, and large streams. In open water a seine must be at least 20 feet long to be effective.

Traps for fishes range from small, barrel-shaped devices made of wire mesh a few feet long, to huge sheets of net (up to several hundred feet on a side) hung in the water. All trap nets use some variation of a conical entrance. The fish enters easily, attracted by the smell or sight of bait (or is guided by the wings of the net). The cone leads to the center of the trap. The passage way is difficult for the fish to find in the exit direction (Figure 12–2).

Gill nets are designed to catch fish by allowing part of the fish's body to slip through the net. When the fish is unable to proceed, and tries to back up, the fine monofilament line catches on its gill covers or fin rays. Trammel nets work in a similar way, except that the fish encounters a small-mesh net sandwiched between two layers of coarse-mesh net. The fish pushes the small-mesh net through one of the openings of the large mesh. It is then trapped in a "bag" of net, and cannot turn around without getting entangled even more. Both of these nets (gill and trammel) are not often allowed as collecting devices because they normally

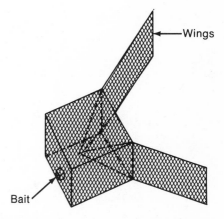

Figure 12–2 Modified trap net showing bait, wings, and conical center passage.

kill all fishes collected. Most fishes collected by many other methods can be released alive.

Electrofishing capitalizes on the fact that a fish in an electrical field will swim erratically toward one of the electrodes. At moderate electrical currents, fishes can be collected with little damage. In small operations, one person "shocks" with a backpack generator, and another person dipnets the stunned fish. Larger operations use powerful generators mounted on boats, with several persons dipnetting.

Chemical methods require that an isolated area, such as a lagoon, tidepool, or embayment be treated. Chemical fishing is increasingly discouraged by fish and game authorities, as it can kill entire local communities.

Hook and line, the classical collecting technique, is still valuable. A variation is the trotline, which is a series of hooks on short leaders hung from a common cord. Typically, the trotline is baited and left overnight near the bottom for catfish or other bottom species.

The Seine Method

In most cases two persons are necessary for operation of a seine. Each end of the lead line is tied a few inches from the bottom of the poles. The float line is then tied to the poles. Both lines should be tied within a few inches of the net mesh (Figure 12-1). The basic principle of a seine is not to "run down" the fish, but to head them into a situation in which the net can be used as a trap.

PROCEDURE:

1. Select, from the shore, a likely place to seine. Plan where the seine will enter the water, where the seine will be worked, and where the operation will end. Once the operation of the net itself is mastered, the most important step of the procedure is accomplished.

MATERIALS

1. Seine
2. Two 6 foot poles
3. Collecting pail with lid
4. Large pans or buckets

2. Enter the water and "clear" the net of tangles. The lead line should be arranged in a smooth arc on the bottom.
3. Move at a slow walk through the area designated. The lead line should be inspected or felt regularly to make sure that it is on the bottom for its entire length.
4. Keeping the lead line on the bottom, drag the lead weights up onto a beach and out of the water. The seined fish are then trapped in the bag of the net.
5. An alternative to step 4, where there are no smooth beaches, is to raise both the lead line and the float line out of the water (like two persons shaking a beach blanket) so that the fish are trapped in the central low area. This technique takes a little practice. It is valuable to have a third person available to pick fish from the net. Raising both lines is also useful when a desired specimen is noticed swimming into the net. If one person shouts "up" and then both persons raise the float and lead lines in the manner just described, an approximation of selective seining may be achieved.
6. Fish specimens should be carefully transferred to large pans or buckets where they may be observed before returning them to their environment.

NOTES:

1. In tangled or confined areas, a short (4 foot) net is most practical.
2. Fish may be observed in large pans or buckets while collection data is being assembled. Care should be taken to avoid excessive handling of fish or handling with dry hands, because this disturbs the mucus slime cover of the fish and leaves them susceptible to bacterial and fungal attack. After observations have been made, specimens should be returned to their environment.
3. Fish should not be preserved unless they are to become part of a responsible collection. Collections for individual class use should be kept to a minimum. Collections of any sort should not be made

without consulting the state fish and game department as to the appropriate procedure.

4. Scales have annular rings roughly equivalent to those of trees which can be used to estimate age (Lagler, Bardach, and Miller, 1962).

Fish Identification Key

The following key is intended as a very simple introduction to the more commonly encountered freshwater fishes. Most of the common forms can be identified to family with a minimum of technical skill. The key is not meant to be complete. For a thorough identification and natural history background of the species or family in question, keys by Eddy (1957) and natural history and general fish biology sources such as Herald (1961) or Trautman (1957) are recommended. General references are provided in the appendix. Local Audubon groups, Sierra Club chapters, Fish and Game Offices (many have a state "Guide to the Fishes"), local colleges and universities, or other nature-oriented groups should be consulted for regional guides. All of the anatomical terms used to identify fishes in the following key are indicated in Figure 12–3.

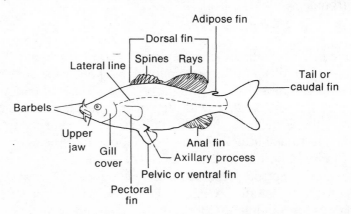

Figure 12–3 Generalized fish, showing anatomical terms used in key to fish (Courtesy of California Department of Fish and Game).

1a   No paired fins. Fish without jaws, mouth circular. Body, eellike. Adult parasitic, attaches with "sucker" mouth to fish, then rasps flesh with teeth on tongue. Responsible for decline of Lake Trout Fishery in Great Lakes region. Makes spawning runs into streams from lakes and ocean. May grow to 2 feet in length. Immature form smaller (6 inches), lives in soft stream substrate, filter-feeding in habit.   **Lamprey** (Figure 1) (Petromyzontidae)

1b   Fish with jaws. *Go to 2*

Figure 1   *Lamprey*

2a   Body, eellike. Dorsal fin continuous with caudal and anal fins. May grow to 3 feet in length. **Freshwater eel** (Figure 2) (Anguillidae)

2b   Body not eellike. Distinct dorsal, anal, and caudal fins.   *Go to 3*

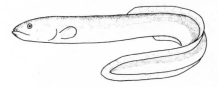

Figure 2   *Freshwater eel*

3a   Fish with bony plates down the side, or large bony, diamond shaped scales covering body, like coat of armor.   *Go to 4*

3b   Fish without obvious lateral bony plates.   *Go to 5*

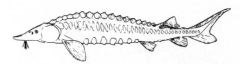

Figure 3   *Sturgeon*

4a   Fish with large bony plates down each side. Four barbels, or fleshy "whiskers" in mouth region.   **Sturgeon** (Figure 3) (Acipenseridae)

4b   Scales hard and diamond shaped. Dorsal and anal fins placed well back. Long, well-armed jaws. May reach 200 pounds and 4 feet in length.   **Gar** (Figure 4) (Lepisosteidae)

Figure 4   *Gar*

5a   Conspicuous bony plate present on "chin" (gular plate). Tail with vertebral support on top edge (Figure 5). Round powerful body, long dorsal fin.   **Bowfin** (Figure 5) (Amiidae)

5b   Chin plate not present. Tail with vertebral support centrally located.   *Go to 6*

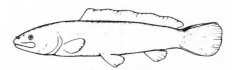

Figure 5   *Bowfin*

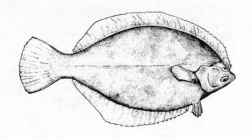

Figure 6　Flounder

6a Both eyes on one side of fish's head. Usually only one side of body pigmented. Swims eyed-side up. Rests on bottom, often covering entire body with substrate except for eyes and mouth. Primarily marine, may move into fresh water. **Flounder** (Figure 6) (Pleuronectidae)

6b Eyes on each side of head. *Go to 7*

7a Adipose fin present (a small fleshy fin posterior to dorsal fin — see Figure 12–3). *Go to 8*

7b Adipose fin absent. *Go to 10*

8a Fleshy barbels on chin, outer edge of upper jaw, and snout region. **Freshwater catfish** (Figures 7–11) (Ictaluridae)

8b Chin without barbels. *Go to 9*

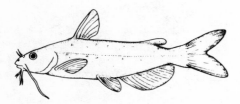

Figure 7　Channel catfish

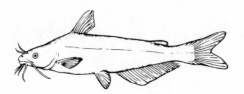

Figure 8　Blue catfish

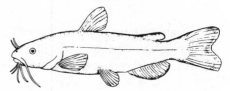

Figure 9　White catfish

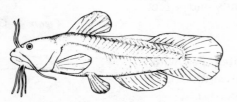

Figure 10　Madtom

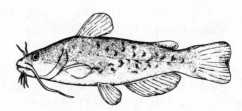

Figure 11　Bullhead

9a Small distinct appendage present above pelvic fins (axillary process). Scales usually fine. Fish brightly colored, or bluish silver in color. **Salmon family** (Figures 12–16) (Salmonidae)

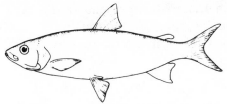

Figure 12   Cisco or whitefish

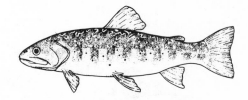

Figure 13   Lake trout

Figure 14   Eastern brook trout

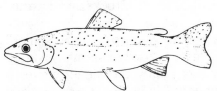
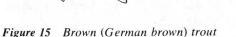

Figure 15   Brown (German brown) trout

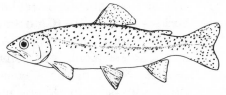

Figure 16   Rainbow trout

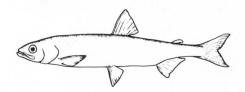

Figure 17   Smelt

9b Axillary process absent. Fish slender and silvery, scales large and coarse. Normally marine with freshwater spawning runs, now landlocked in many places. **Smelt** (Figure 17) (Osmeridae)

10a Belly with sharp serrated keel, fish laterally compressed. Silvery in color with large scales that fall out easily on handling. Various species introduced as forage for gamefish. **Shad** (Figure 18) (Clupeidae)

10b Belly without sharp serrated keel. *Go to 11*

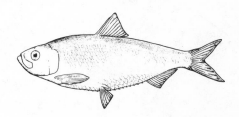

Figure 18   Shad

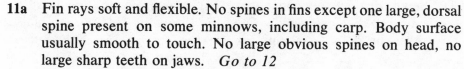

11a Fin rays soft and flexible. No spines in fins except one large, dorsal spine present on some minnows, including carp. Body surface usually smooth to touch. No large obvious spines on head, no large sharp teeth on jaws. *Go to 12*

11b **One or more** of the following characteristics present: (a) fin rays with hard, sharp spines, (b) if scales, rough to the touch, (c) head with obvious spines, particularly on gill cover, (d) jaw teeth obvious, strong, and sharp. *Go to 17*

12a Mouth without teeth. *Go to 13*

12b Mouth with teeth. *Go to 14*

13a Mouth bordered by thick, fleshy lips, usually directed downward. Many species with various body shapes. Normally bottom feeders, grazing upon aquatic insect larvae, algal scum of rocks and detritus. **Suckers** (Figure 19) (Catostomidae)

13b Mouth without fleshy lips. Appearance, goldfish-like or "shiner" like. Largest family of freshwater fishes, containing many varied species. Many of the species in this family are small, white or silver with black markings, and schooling in habit. **Carp/minnow/ shiner family** (Figures 20–22) (Cyprinidae)

Figure 19   Suckers

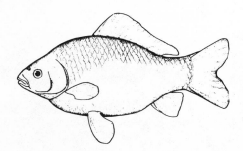

Figure 20   Goldfish

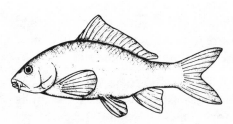

Figure 21   Carp

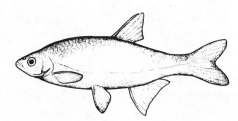

Figure 22   Golden shiner

14a One dorsal fin present. *Go to 15*
14b Two dorsal fins present. *Go to 16*

15a Small fishes, mouth with teeth. Male smaller, with anal fin modified into copulatory organ (gonopodium). If adult, female with "brood patch," a pigmented region at posterior of abdomen. **Live bearers** (Figures 23–24) (Poeciliidae)

15b Mouth with teeth, lower jaw extending anterior to upper jaw. Small to medium size. Mouth opens upward, most species adapted for surface existence. **Killifish** (Figures 25–26) (Cyprinodontidae)

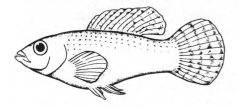

Figure 23   Sailfin molly

male

female

Figure 24   Mosquito fish

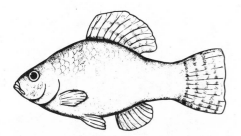

Figure 25   Pupfish

Figure 26   Killifish

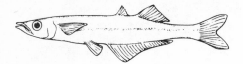

Figure 27   Silversides

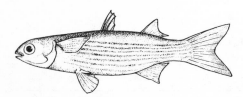

Figure 28   Mullets

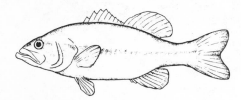

Figure 29   Largemouth black bass

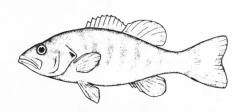

Figure 30   Smallmouth bass

16a   Slender, silvery body. Lower jaw usually extending anterior to upper jaw. Body usually with thin, obvious "tin foil" looking band down lateral surface. Dorsal fins widely separated. **Silversides** (Figure 27) (Atherinidae)

16b   Thick, often silvery body. Lower jaw does not extend anterior to upper jaw. Eye partly covered by jellylike thick membrane. Uncovered portion of eye shaped in a vertical slit. Marine, but common in tide water areas and into coastal rivers. **Mullets** (Figure 28) (Mugilidae)

17a   First (spinous) dorsal fin separated from second (soft-rayed) dorsal fin, or nearly separated with first dorsal as high as the second dorsal. **Perch, walleye and temperate basses.** *Go to 23*

17b   Spiny and soft-rayed portions of dorsal fin joined. (If dorsals seem separated, first dorsal not as high as second dorsal.) *Go to 18*

18a   Body oval to round in lateral profile. Body compressed from side to side, colorful, often with blue or red tab on gill cover. Or fish may be basslike, heavy bodied, dark green-gray in color. If dorsal notched, first dorsal not as high as second dorsal. **Sunfish family** (Figures 29–35) (Centrarchidae) includes sunfish, crappies, bluegills, and freshwater basses.

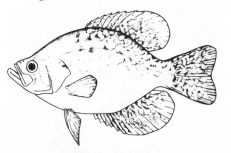

Figure 31   Black crappie

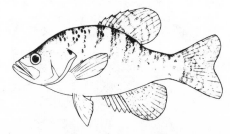

Figure 32   White crappie

Figure 33   *Bluegill*

Figure 34   *Pumpkinseed*

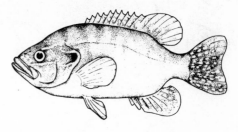

Figure 35   *Green sunfish*

18b   Body not compressed from side to side. No obvious tabs on gill cover.   *Go to 19*

19a   Body elongate, dorsal and anal fins set posteriorly, teeth obvious. Jaws duck-like or elongate.   *Go to 20*

19b   Body not elongate, but rounded in profile from side or above. Jaws not duck-like or elongate.   *Go to 21*

20a   Medium to large fish (1 to 75 pounds). Long body with dorsal and anal fins set posteriorly (near tail). Jaws shaped like duck's bill. Powerful, with strong teeth. Pike family.   **Muskellunge** (Figure 36) (Esocidae)

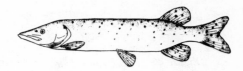

Figure 36   *Muskellunge*

20b   Body elongate, torpedo shaped, with dorsal and anal fins set posteriorly. Jaws very long and tapered, lined with fine, sharp teeth. Surface habits. Marine, moving into estuaries and coastal rivers.   **Needlefish** (Figure 37) (Belonidae)

Figure 37   *Needlefish*

21a   Head relatively large, broad and depressed. Eyes close together, at anterior of head. Gill cover with at least one spine or bony process. Fish rests for long periods in one spot on the bottom, with pectoral fins spread, fan-like. Moves abruptly.   **Sculpin** (Figure 38) (Cottidae)

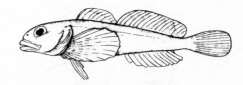

Figure 38   *Sculpin*

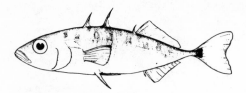

Figure 39   *Stickleback*

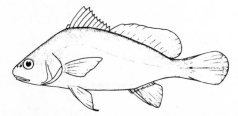

Figure 40   *Freshwater drum*

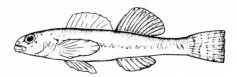

Figure 41   *Darter*

21b   Head and body of fish compressed from side to side. Eyes well separated. Pectoral fins not large and fan-like.   *Go to 22*

22a   Small (2–3 inches) fish with series of 3 to 9 separate spines preceding the dorsal fin.   **Stickleback** (Figure 39) (Gasterosteidae)

22b   Fish with blunt, squared-off snout. Lateral line extending well out onto caudal fin. Mostly marine with many species moving into coastal rivers. One freshwater form.   **Freshwater drum** (Figure 40) (Sciaenidae)

23a   Anal fin with 2 spines, gill cover without well-developed spine. Medium sized, yellow with 6 to 9 black vertical bands; **or** elongate, medium sized to 24 in. with many fanglike teeth in mouth; **or** small (less than 6 in.) with round body and bottom living habits (rests on pectoral fins when not swimming, moves in quick spurts, with long pauses in between).   **Perch, walleye, and darters** (Figures 41–42) (Percidae)

23b   Anal fin with 3 spines. Gill cover with single obvious spine. Body with 7 or 8 longitudinal dark stripes. Widely introduced as game fish. Found in marine, estuarine, fresh, and impounded (landlocked) waters. Striped bass. Other exclusively freshwater forms are the white bass and yellow bass. They are much heavier-bodied fishes. In the striped bass, the depth of body is less than one-third the distance of snout to caudal fin base.   **Striped bass** (Figure 44) (Percichthyidae)

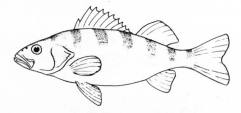

Figure 42   *Yellow perch*

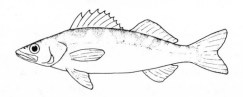

Figure 43   *Walleye*

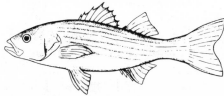

Figure 44   *Striped bass*

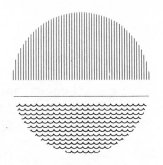

13. Benthos

As one studies the animals of the bottom (benthos), it soon becomes evident that there are many adaptations for survival. The more obvious are concerned with feeding, and fall into the categories of grazing, predation, detritus (organic debris) feeding, and filter feeding. Feeding, as well as other adaptations, may or may not coincide with the systematic (evolutionary) arrangement of the animals. Zoologists, out of necessity, use an evolutionary system to organize the animal kingdom. Even so, it is very valuable to be able to visualize a system organized by function (for example, the common factors found in filter feeders, no matter what their evolutionary standing). Such a study develops an understanding of an animal's way of living, related to the way it is shaped or the way it moves. The study of such relationships is called functional anatomy and illustrates the inseparable nature of the biotic (living) and abiotic (nonliving) aspects of the environment.

As a rule, bottom animals can be divided, on the basis of their location, into two groups: active types that dwell on the surface, represented by the crayfish, are called epi (upon) benthos; and less active types that live buried beneath the sand or mud, represented by the freshwater clam, are called the infauna. Most of the predators (crayfish) and grazing forms (snails) are epibenthos, and most of the filter feeders (clams) are infauna. Other (soft substrate) infauna ingest the substrate for digestible materials, like the earthworm.

Faunal communities of the inshore, shallow areas will normally be more diverse than those of the deeper lake bottom. The shallow regions may have various snails, clams, insects, and crustaceans. If the deep water has low organic content, then the benthos below that water may be a reduced version of the species distribution in the shallow region. If the deeper muds are organic, with low oxygen levels, the species found in inshore regions will often not be present in those muds and the bottom inhabitants will often be great numbers of midge or other dipteran larvae. If decomposition occurs in the absence of oxygen, anaerobic bacteria may produce hydrogen sulfide or methane gas. The line of demarcation between oxygenated and unoxygenated water is easily spotted by a diver. The oxygenated side of the line has a benthic community, the unoxygenated side has a blackened lifeless substrate, or species adapted for anaerobic conditions.

Collecting Methods

Screen Series

In most collecting for bottom infauna, the bottom material is collected and then placed upon a series of graded screens. The mud is washed through the screens with a water jet. The screens range in mesh size from the largest (coarse hardware cloth) on top to the smallest (fine window screen or smaller) on the bottom. Actual mesh size of screens is unimportant as the series is simply a method to separate objects from the substrate. Each screen then retains a particular size range of animals. Such screen series can easily be constructed using 2 × 4 lumber made into nesting squares, with the screening nailed across the top (Figure 13–1).

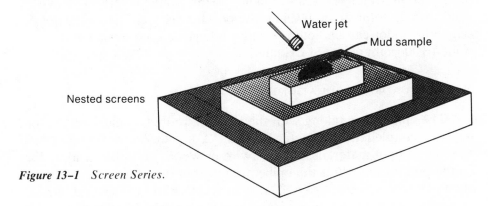

Figure 13–1 *Screen Series.*

FOOT-OPERATED CORE SAMPLER

There are several effective methods for collection of near shore, bottom materials. The time-tested technique is digging with a shovel. More material in less time is obtained in this way (remember earlier precautions on consideration of environment). However, shovels are not quantitative. In order to determine the number of creatures per volume (usually cubic meter) or the number of creatures per area of bottom, a quantitative collecting device is required.

A foot-operated core sampler (Figure 13–2) is simple and effective. It is placed on the bottom, open-end down (with the stopper out of its hole). The operator's foot is then placed on the top of the sampler, and enough weight is shifted to the device to press it into the substrate. When the device is sunk to its top, the stopper is replaced in the hole. The entire device is then lifted up by the handle. The sampler comes out of the substrate with a core of bottom material inside. As the samples are taken, it is important to record the location of the sample with respect to current, present water level, and other possible water levels as shown by windrows or color differences on the beach or shore. The volume of the sample cylinder can be determined by filling the core device with water from a 1000 ml graduated cylinder.

METER QUADRAT (AQUATIC)

The epibenthos (along with the inshore, rooted, aquatic vegetation) is often sampled with a meter quadrat. A square-meter frame is constructed of light materials, such as wire or wood. It is placed at random on the bottom and all of the epibenthos within the area enclosed by the quadrat is collected or counted. It is instructive to take several samples in similar areas to get an idea of sample variation. Large sample variation (error) indicates a need for measuring larger quadrats or using the arithmetic mean of several smaller quadrats. When a sampling technique has been determined, one area is compared to other areas with different depths, substrate types, exposures to water action, light, etc. Usually the results of such a survey are expressed in numbers of individuals or as grams of each species, wet or dry weight per square meter. Wet weight is easiest to work with. It involves weighing a beaker of water, then dropping in the material in question and noting the resultant increase in weight. It also allows volume to be determined. A more accurate but more laborious method is to measure dry weight. The material is dried to eliminate the variable water content of the specimens and then weighed.

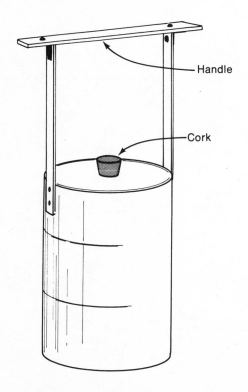

— Handle

— Cork

Figure 13–2 Foot-operated Core Sampler.

SURBER STREAM SAMPLER

A variation of the meter quadrat, for use in streams, is the Surber stream sampler (Figure 13–3). The square portion of the sampler is placed at random on the stream bottom; then the substrate within the frame is agitated. The creatures living within the frame are suspended in the water by the agitation. Then the current washes them into a bag held open at the downstream side of the frame, where they are held until recovered for examination. A series of samples compared to physical conditions of the sampling sites allow the biological/environmental associations to be visualized.

Direction
of
current

Figure 13–3   Surber Stream Sampler.

EKMAN DREDGE

In the deeper areas, sampling must be done remotely, which requires the use of equipment lowered on a line. The standard device for the usual soft bottom found in freshwater lakes and large streams is the Ekman dredge (Figure 13–4). It is lowered to the bottom in the "cocked" position (jaws open). A sliding weight, or messenger, is then sent down the line, causing the device to bite a sample out of the bottom with a pair of spring-loaded jaws. Other modifications of the spring-loaded jaw are designed for different bottom textures. Ekman and other dredges capture slow-moving epibenthos and the relatively shallow-living infauna.

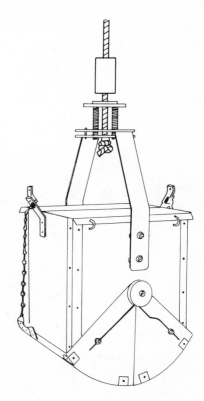

Figure 13–4   Ekman Dredge.

GRAVITY CORE SAMPLER

The core sampler (Figure 13–5) is a heavy tube with a one-way valve at the top. The tube is allowed to plunge down through the water until it strikes the bottom, where its inertia drives the device into the substrate. When the operator begins to draw the tube up, its contents are prevented (usually) from sliding out by the one-way valve at its top. The core sample contains a section through the bottom layers, and provides material for analysis of the history of the lake bottom.

Benthos Identification Key

As in the other keys, the key to benthic organisms is designed solely as an introduction to the animals composing bottom communities. This category, more than any other, seems to need a simple means of introducing the major groups of animals. Once a basic familiarity with the invertebrates is attained, there is a wealth of information available on invertebrate biology (Barnes, 1968), keys (Pennak, 1953; Ward and Whipple, 1966), and natural history (Buchsbaum, 1938). This key does not apply to marine organisms. General references are provided in the appendix. Local colleges and universities should be consulted for regional guides. Scientific names are used where no convenient common name is available.

1a Material forming a fuzzy, stringy, spongy, or slimy coating over the substrate. No particular form involved, and no obvious internal structure. *Go to 4*

1b Gelatinous glob of clear material, with various inclusions. *Go to 5*

1c Organism showing definite form, with evidence of internal organization. *Go to 2*

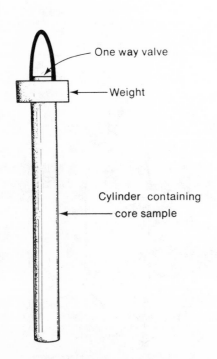

One way valve

Weight

Cylinder containing core sample

Figure 13–5   Gravity Core Sampler.

2a Organization radially symmetrical (organized around a central focal point). *Go to 3*

2b Organization bilaterally (right and left sides similarly organized) symmetrical. *Go to 6*

3a Animal sponge-like, shaped like a vase. **Grantia** (sponge) (Figure 1)

3b Animal stalked, with arms usually ringing the mouth at the terminal portion of the stalk. Stinging cells (nematocysts) present for food capture. **Hydra** (Figure 2)

4a Material, stringy and hairlike, often in relatively swift portions of stream. Under microscope, diatom nature of strands may be determined. **Filamentous diatoms** (Figure 3)

4b Material forms a slimy coating over substrate. Structure not easily visible under microscope. **Bacterial scum**

4c Material fuzzy. Under microscope, rings of tentacles (polyps) are visible, arranged on plantlike stalks. May be branched. Living structures are sensitive to touch. **Moss animals** (phylum: Bryozoa) (Figure 4)

4d Material spongy. Under microscope pores are visible, surrounded by typical spongy mat with irregular surface. **Encrusting sponge**

5a Rather loose glob or tube of gelatinous material containing well-spaced, small (2–6 mm), usually dark-colored eggs. Surface of eggs often with segmented appearance. Often a transparent layer of material surrounding the egg. **Eggs of amphibia**

5b Firm globs of gelatinous material attached to rocks, twigs, etc. Light-colored eggs or developing embryos spaced throughout. **Snail eggs**

Figure 1 Grantia

Figure 2 Hydra

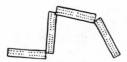

Figure 3 Filamentous diatom

Figure 4 Bryozoa

Figure 5   Water bear (subphylum: Tardigrada)

Figure 6   Water mite (order: Hydracarina)

Figure 7   Roundworm (class: Nematoda)

6a   Body, wormlike.   *Go to 7*

6b   Body of creature with hard external shell, and jointed appendages. Some insects may be various in form (maggotlike, pupa, or encased in sand grains).   **Crustaceans** and **aquatic insects**   *Go to 10*

6c   Creature is a snail, clam, or limpet (snail-like animal under a volcano-shaped, single shell). Hard shell, with soft-bodied animal inside.   *Go to 16*

6d   Creature with cylindrical body, more or less distinct head, and 4 pairs of appendages, each ending in rather distinct claws. Microscopic to 1.5 mm in length.   **Water bears** (subphylum: Tardigrada) (Figure 5)

6e   Rapidly moving, often brightly colored (red, orange) spiderlike animal. Size, 1–4 mm in length. Four legs obvious, two others less distinct. Differ from spiders in that head and abdomen is a single, round, globular structure.   **Water mites** (order: Hydracarina) (Figure 6)

6f   Body: maggotlike or grublike.   **Beetle, diptera** or **fly larvae**
Semi-rigid case often with mummy-like structures, representing folded appendages, visible ventrally.   **Pupae** (Chu, 1949)

7a   Body of the worm segmented. Segments may require magnification to be seen, or may be indicated by regular sets of lateral bristles.   *Go to 9*

7b   Body of the worm not segmented.   *Go to 8*

8a   Body slender, tapered, and covered with a dense cuticle. Microscopic to 1 mm in length. Motion of living animal a violent thrashing, in which the body is bowed, end to end, then rapidly straightened and bowed in the alternate direction. Most species have a cement gland posteriorly located for temporary attachment to substrate. Huge numbers can be found in almost any benthic or periphyton (surface of large plant material) sample. Taxonomy is very difficult. Related groups parasitic in man and other animals. **Free-living roundworms** (class: Nematoda) (Figure 7)

8b Body smooth or textured, but not segmented. Long (10 cm to 70 cm) slender worms. Length and coloration variable. Always coiled and in twisted position, and often observed writhing around. The smaller males often swim in an undulating manner. Reproduction involves "balls" of worms in a writhing mass composed of both sexes. Habitat is either standing water or the near shore area of streams. Name derived from the common presence of the worm in stock tanks. **Horsehair worms** (class: Nematomorpha) (Figure 8)

8c Worm elongate, flattened, often with a "head" indicated anteriorly by small, pointed, earlike structures visible in the dorsal view. Eyespots are present between the earlike structures. Size, 4 to 30 mm in length. Various colors, but commonly dark colored. Most are photonegative (avoid light), found under rocks and other objects in a wide variety of aquatic habitats. **Flatworms** (class: Turbellaria) (Figure 9)

9a Active, powerful worm, microscopic to macroscopic length, 0.5 to 30 mm. Regular sets of bristles (setae) positioned laterally along the body. Moves like an earthworm. Probes and feeds by thrusting anterior of body into organic debris. **Aquatic earthworms** (class: Oligochaeta) (Figure 10)

9b Small, brown or reddish worms with tapered ends. In nature, reside in very rich organic substrate. Found in dense aggregations, individuals extend a large portion of their body out of a hole and wave vigorously in whiplike motion. Considered a pollution indicator. Sold as live fish food in most tropical fish stores. **Tubifex worms** (class: Oligochaeta) (Figure 11)

Figure 8   *Horsehair worm (class: Nematomorpha)*

Figure 9   *Flatworm (class: Turbellaria)*

Figure 10   *Aquatic earthworm (class: Oligochaeta)*

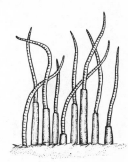

Figure 11   *Tubifex worms (class: Oligochaeta)*

9c   Flattened but thick bodied, roughly tear-drop shaped when contracted. Size from 5–10 mm to 30 cm or more. Anterior sucker surrounds mouth. Body color variable, often very colorful with patterns of bands, stripes, or spots. Often good swimmers, using an undulating movement; also move by inchworm movements, using oral sucker. Attaches to various animals with sucker to suck blood. Different species will parasitize different groups of animals, ranging from snails and amphibia to birds and mammals. Prefer shores of quiet waters. Normally inactive during daylight, but will come out from under rock hiding places with water disturbance, or blood in the water.   **Leeches** (blood suckers) (class: Hirudinea) (Figure 12)

Figure 12   Leech (class: Hirudinea)

10a   Animal compressed laterally, body composed of obvious articulated segments. Size, 5 to 20 mm in length. Commonly found on rooted or floating vegetation in shallow, usually cold, well-oxygenated waters.   **Amphipods** — sand fleas, beach hoppers, water fleas (e.g., *Gammarus*) (order: Amphipoda) (Figure 13)

10b   Five pairs of appendages under a cephalothorax (fused segments composing combined head and thorax region). The abdominal region, a series of articulated plates ending in a tail "fin" made of thin, flexible, chitinous material. Shrimp or crayfish appearance. *Go to 15*

10c   Insects. Since all stages of insect life cycle may be present, form may be various. Adults with 3 pairs of appendages.   *Go to 11*

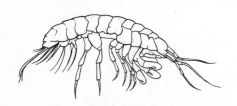

Figure 13   Amphipod

11a Body of insect, maggotlike. No jointed thoracic legs. **Larvae of flies, mosquitos, midges** (order: Diptera) (Chu, 1949)

11b Body with jointed thoracic legs. *Go to 12*

12a Body with long, segmented appendages at rear. *Go to 13*

12b Body with no long, segmented appendages at rear. *Go to 14*

13a Body with two posterior appendages, legs end with paired claws. **Larvae of stoneflies** (order: Plecoptera) (Figure 14)

13b Body with three, or rarely two, posterior appendages. Legs end with a single claw. **Larvae of mayfly** (order: Ephemeroptera) (Figure 15)

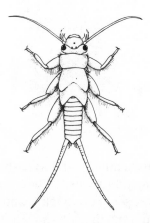

Figure 14 Stonefly nymph (order: Plecoptera)

Figure 15 Mayfly larva

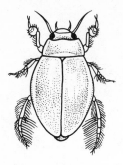

Figure 16   *Predaceous   Diving   Beetle* (*Dytiscidae*)

14a   Dorsal surface of body covered with two hard, usually shiny, wing covers. Wing covers fit tightly together joining at midline of body where they open to expose wings beneath. Air breathing. These beetles come to the surface to collect an air bubble, which is carried under the wing covers or as a thin sheet of air held by fine hairs (gives appearance of silver coating over beetle's body). Gas exchange takes place through boundaries of the bubble, allowing insect to stay submerged for long periods of time. Capable of inflicting painful bite.   **Aquatic beetles** (order: Coleoptera) (Figures 16–18)

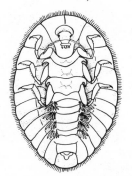
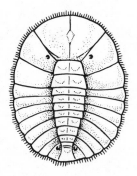

Figure 18   *Water   penny   (dorsal/ventral)* (*Psephenidae*)

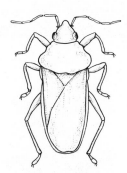

Figure 19   *Velvet   water   bug* (*Hebridae*)

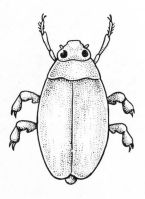

Figure 17   *Whirligig beetle (Gyrinidae)*

14b   Two pairs of formed wings. First pair leathery at base, the rest membranous. Second pair entirely membranous. When folded, wings give the impression of an "X" crossing the back. Almost all forms with powerful grasping legs, and long, dagger-shaped mouth parts. Some forms are good swimmers, others creep on submerged vegetation. Some forms (Belostomatidae) are active, strong swimming predators. Capable of painful bite.   **True bugs** (order: Hemiptera) (Figures 19–26)

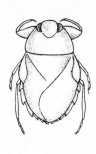

Figure 20 *Creeping water bug*
(*Naucoridae*)

Figure 21 *Water scorpion*
(*Nepidae*)

Figure 22 *Giant water bug*
(*Belostomatidae*)

Figure 23 *Marsh treader*
(*Hydrometridae*)

Figure 24 *Water strider*
(*Gerridae*)

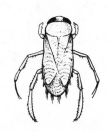

Figure 25 *Water boatman*
(*Corixidae*)

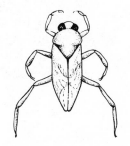

Figure 26 *Back swimmer*
(*Notonectidae*)

Figure 27 *Hellgrammite*
(*order: Megaloptera*)

14c Each segment of abdomen with stout or hairy lateral process. Body ending in a tapering filament or hooked leg pair. Body heavy, elongate, 20 to 100 mm in length. Preferred by fishermen as bait. Found under stones in streams and ponds. **Hellgrammites: larvae of Dobson fly, etc.** (order: Megaloptera) (Figure 27)

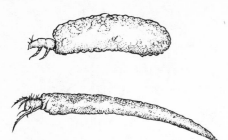

Figure 28 Caddisfly larva (order: Trichoptera)

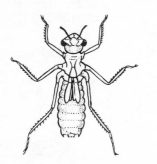

Figure 29 Dragonfly nymph (sub-order: Anisoptera)

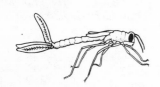

Figure 30 Damselfly nymph (sub-order: Zygoptera)

14d Animal living in case constructed from sand particles or other immediately available materials, such as plant fragments. Case held together in a conical or cylinderical form by mucus secretions. Often locally abundant in fertile streams.   **Caddisfly larvae** (order: Trichoptera) (Figure 28)

14e Stout heavy body, with six legs. Mouth parts formed into scoop-like structure, that extends forward or folds to cover lower face. **Dragonfly nymph** (sub-order: Anisoptera) (Figure 29)

Larvae as above, but also with three flat, external, gill plates extending from the posterior of the abdomen. **Damselfly nymph** (sub-order: Zygoptera) (Figure 30)

15a Creature large, 15 to 130 mm in length, with well-developed pincers. Body, rounded in cross-section.   **Crayfish** (order: Decapoda) (Figure 31)

15b Creature smaller, usually to 60 mm (some species large, to 240 mm) in length. Pincers reduced to small forceplike structures. Head with prominent, forward-directed spine.   **Freshwater shrimp, grass shrimp** (order: Decapoda) (Figure 32)

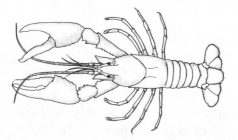

Figure 31 Crayfish (order: Decapoda)

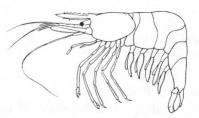

Figure 32 Freshwater shrimp (order: Decapoda)

16a Animal inside a pair of hinged "clam" shells. **Bivalves**—freshwater clams and mussels (class: Pelecypoda) (Figures 33–36)

16b Shell in one part. May be coiled (snail shell) or shaped like volcano. **Freshwater snails and limpets** (class: Gastropoda) (Figures 37–42)

Figure 33 Corbicula   *Figure 34* Anodonta   *Figure 35* Margaritifera   *Figure 36* Sphaerium

Figure 37 Helisoma   *Figure 38* Physa   *Figure 39* Ancyclus

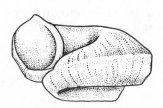
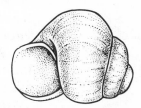

Figure 40 Viviparus   *Figure 41* Valvata   *Figure 42* Amnicola

14.
Environmental
Profile

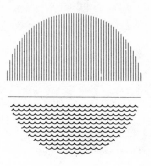

The preceding laboratory evaluations are all means of determining single aspects of the conditions of an environment. The environmental profile is an effort to maintain the ecosystem viewpoint while dealing with the necessary unit approaches of field work. It is a method of putting things together. It should assist development of the ability to appreciate the environment as a whole.

An ecosystem has been defined as the totality of interactions of the biotic (living) and abiotic (nonliving) environment. In attempts to evaluate the nature of an aquatic ecosystem, certain factors are valuable as indicators. Indicators are environmental factors that, in certain amounts or concentrations, are closely associated with particular environmental conditions. The environmental profile is a graphic presentation of some of these indicators:

OXYGEN: A great deal can be learned about an environment by measuring oxygen concentrations. Animal activity and plant activity in dark conditions consume oxygen. Photosynthesis of plants increases oxygen concentrations. Differences in oxygen concentrations between lighted (high dissolved oxygen) and unlighted (low dissolved oxygen) levels indicate a biologically rich environment. A good deal of decomposition is probably going on in the deeper layers of such waters.

CARBON DIOXIDE: A by-product of metabolic activity, carbon dioxide in high concentrations indicates large populations of active organisms.

TURBIDITY: If organic in nature, turbidity may indicate a high density of microscopic organisms, or the remains of plants and animals in the water. Even inorganic suspended sediments will reduce light penetration and restrict the productive zone to shallow depths.

BOD (Biochemical Oxygen Demand): BOD is another means of evaluating the amount of organic materials in water and the potential loss of oxygen to the system. BOD is high in eutrophic environments and low in oligotrophic environments.

DIVERSITY INDEX: The numbers and kinds of resident plants and animals are of value in determining the basic nature of an environment. If there are many individuals of a few species, conditions are indicated that will favor the presence of organisms having a wide range of tolerance. Under such conditions, the environment is probably eutrophic. A few organisms that include many species indicate an oligotrophic environment. Organisms in oligotrophic environments have narrow ranges of tolerance for many factors.

NUTRIENT SALTS: Compounds of nitrogen, phosphorus, and other elements are the raw materials necessary for plant growth. These nutrients are normally limiting factors if found in low concentrations.

DIVERSITY INDEX

Generally, in ecological systems, a complex biological community connotes a stable environmental situation. Evaluation of an ecosystem can often be accomplished by measuring the number of species in the biological community. One way of expressing this relationship is Simpson's (1949) Diversity Index.

$$\frac{(\text{total \#'s of organisms})^2}{(\#\text{'s of species } a)^2 + (\#\text{'s of species } b)^2 + (\#\text{'s of species } c)^2 + \text{etc.}}$$

or

$$\frac{N^2}{\Sigma(n)^2}$$

This index increases as the numbers of species increase in a population of a given size. A sample of 30 individuals, all the same species, has an index of 1. A sample of 30 that has 3 species (10 individuals each) has an index of 3.0. The diversity index is a biological indication of the complexity and, thus, often of the stability of an environment. A high index (many different species with few numbers) implies a stable, oligotrophic or mesotrophic environment. A low index (few species among many organisms) implies a eutrophic or otherwise unstable environment.

Each of these factors may have values typical for a particular environment. An environmental profile assembles the diagnostic factors and shows the interrelations of those factors. The nature of the assembled factors helps to identify particular kinds of environments. Values for a particular environmental factor are plotted on the profile chart indicating the range of high and low extremes. The general nature of the environmental profiles of three different kinds of environments are as follows:

Oligotrophic environment (Figure 14–1):   These very clear waters are characterized by high stability (that is, narrow ranges of most conditions). They are nutrient poor (low concentrations of nutrient salts) with small but diverse populations of plants and animals. The oligotrophic profile is narrow and to the left of the chart.

Mesotrophic environment (Figure 14–2):   These waters are characterized by intermediate values of most factors. Ranges of extremes of these factors fall between the ranges found in oligotrophic and eutrophic classifications. Mesotrophic environments may have characteristics approaching oligotrophic conditions early in the growing season. They may approximate eutrophic conditions late in the growing season in temperate climates. The mesotrophic profile has intermediate width and is near the center of the chart.

Eutrophic environment (Figure 14–3):   These usually turbid, nutrient-rich waters are characterized by a general lack of stability (wide ranges of extremes of most factors). Variations exist from one sampling site to another, from one time of day to another, and especially between surface and bottom regions. Plant and animal populations are abundant and composed of a few species of a tolerant nature. The eutrophic profile is wide and jagged, and is located to the right of the chart.

Environmental Profile: Oligotrophic — Lake Tahoe

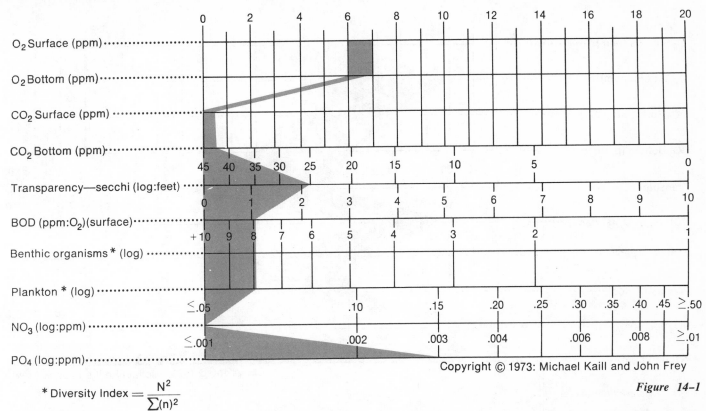

* Diversity Index $= \dfrac{N^2}{\sum(n)^2}$

Figure 14–1

Figures 14–1, 14–2, 14–3   *Values of environmental conditions increase from left to right, with the exception of secchi transparency, and the diversity indices, which increases from right to left. Generally, sterile environments will register toward the left end of the diagram (Figure 14–1: Oligotrophic Environment). Plots for values should, when connected, approximate a straight vertical profile. Richer environments will register toward the right end of the diagram. As the profile moves to the right, the range of values for a given factor (width of profile) should increase. Also, the profiles may become jagged in appearance. A "spike," or a particular factor that departs radically from the other values of the column is worth investigation (Figure 14–3: Eutrophic Environment). A profile can be assembled from data over a period of time, so that departures from the assembled profile, representing environmental shifts, may be determined and investigated.*

Environmental Profile: Mesotrophic — Davis Lake

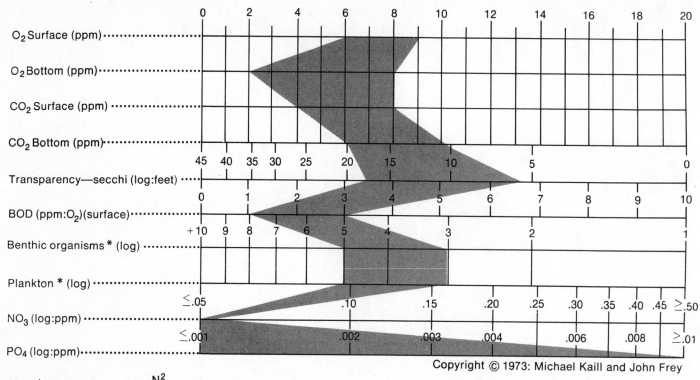

* Diversity Index $= \dfrac{N^2}{\sum(n)^2}$

Figure 14–2

Copyright © 1973: Michael Kaill and John Frey

Figures 14–1, 14–2, 14–3   Values of environmental conditions increase from left to right, with the exception of secchi transparency, and the diversity indices, which increases from right to left. Generally, sterile environments will register toward the left end of the diagram (Figure 14–1: Oligotrophic Environment). Plots for values should, when connected, approximate a straight vertical profile. Richer environments will register toward

Environmental Profile: Eutrophic — Clear Lake

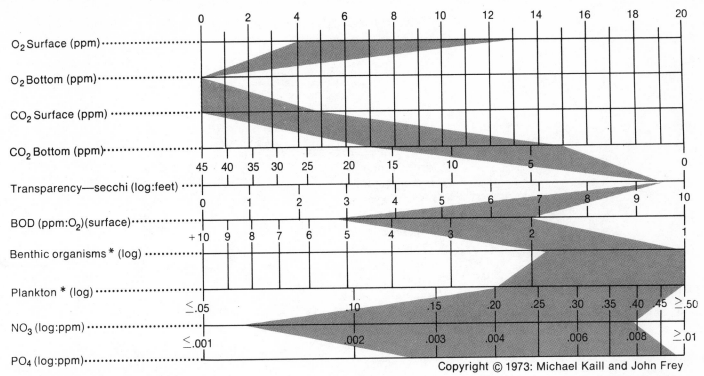

Figure 14–3

Copyright © 1973: Michael Kaill and John Frey

* Diversity Index $= \dfrac{N^2}{\Sigma(n)^2}$

the right end of the diagram. As the profile moves to the right, the range of values for a given factor (width of profile) should increase. Also, the profiles may become jagged in appearance. A "spike," or a particular factor that departs radically from the other values of the column is worth investigation (Figure 14–3: Eutrophic Environment). A profile can be assembled from data over a period of time, so that departures from the assembled profile, representing environmental shifts, may be determined and investigated.

Sample Profile

We will assemble a sample profile based on composite data from Lake Davis (Table 14–1).

Table 14–1 *Data from field trips* (*data taken from field note sheet*)

Time	7:00 A.M.	7:00 P.M.	7:00 P.M.
Date	June 15th Collection A	June 15th Collection B	August 17th Collection C
O_2 surface (ppm)	6	8	9
O_2 bottom (ppm)	3	3	2
CO_2 surface (ppm)	5	8	4
CO_2 bottom (ppm)	6	8	10
Transparency-secchi (ft.)	7	6	17
BOD surface (ppm: O_2)	1	3	1
Benthic organisms*	4	3	6
Plankton*	3.5	4	5
NO_3 (ppm)	.01	.01	.00
PO_4 (ppm)	.003	.006	.008

*Diversity Index

Procedure for assembling environmental profile data with sample profiles based on composite data from Lake Davis:

1. Shortly after daybreak* collect data. If data for all categories cannot be collected, profile may be constructed with incomplete data.
2. Plot the data (e.g., Collection A, Table 14–1) on an environmental profile chart (Figure 14–4a). Connect the points.

---

*Collection at daybreak and dusk will probably reveal largest ranges of factors for 24 hour period, reflecting the result of nighttime and daytime conditions, respectively.

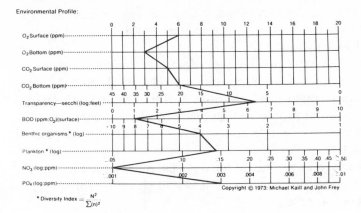

Figure 14-4a

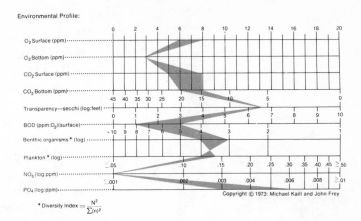

Figure 14-4b

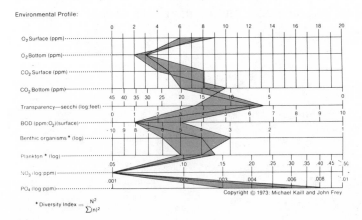

Figure 14-4c

Figure 14-4 *Environmental profiles constructed from three days of field trip data (Table 14-1).*

3. Collect data in the evening, near dusk. Plot the data (e.g., Collection B, Table 14–1) on the same environmental profile chart. Connect points (Figure 14–4b).

4. If the space between extremes for every factor is shaded, an environmental profile for the 24 hour period is produced (Figure 14–4b).

5. If plots are made through one season (e.g., June through August), a seasonal environmental profile can be made by shading the space between the extremes (e.g., Collections A, B, C of Table 14–1 plotted on Figure 14–4c).

6. The extremes for a year's data (in most cases, represented by winter vs. late summer conditions), when plotted and shaded, represent the total environmental profile (Figure 14–2).

7. A blank environmental profile chart is provided on the inside of the back cover. Students are encouraged to trace or copy the chart, to be used as an overlay on the three example profiles (Figures 14–1, 14–2, 14–3). Other uses include a comparison of the profile of a lake or pond from one season to the next, comparisons of lab systems (i.e., aquarium) to lake or pond, and comparisons of lakes or ponds to one another.

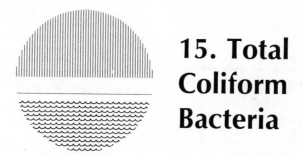

15. Total Coliform Bacteria

The coliform test is an accepted method for determining if drinking water or water supplies are contaminated with sewage. Coliform bacteria can only live in the intestinal tracts of man and other warm-blooded mammals. Up to 50% of fecal material is coliform bacteria. Coliform bacteria are not harmful to man, but their presence indicates sewage contamination and the potential presence of the organisms causing diseases, such as typhoid fever and dysentery. If coliform bacteria are absent, it is not likely that a health hazard exists due to sewage contamination.

In testing for coliform bacteria, aseptic techniques must be practiced to avoid sample contamination.

Millipore Method*

Sample Collection

Samples may be collected from natural waters such as ground water, streams, lakes (near shore, deep, or shallow). Samples may also be taken from domestic water supplies, and even sewage effluent.

Care should be taken in handling highly contaminated waters. Coliform tests should be run within a few hours of the time of collection. Fecal coliform bacteria do not live long outside of the intestinal system.

Sterilization and Preparation of Equipment

procedure (consult diagram):

1. Place the 250 ml funnel, filter base, pipette, and 100 ml beaker in boiling water for 3 minutes.
2. Dip tips of tongs in alcohol and flame (pass through the flame of a bunsen burner several times). Using the sterile tongs, remove the equipment from the boiling water and place on a clean paper towel to drip dry.
3. Connect filter base to receiver flask. Avoid touching filter support.
4. Flame the forceps and allow to cool. Remove a millipore gridded filter from the sterile envelope and center the filter directly on the filter support. (Use forceps to handle filter.)
5. Firmly screw the millipore funnel onto the filter base. Position funnel cover on top of funnel, and cap Luer ports on the funnel cover.
6. Firmly insert the tip of the hand vacuum assembly into the one-way

---

MATERIALS

1. Millipore Sterifil Filtration Apparatus**
2. Rubber hose and hand vacuum assembly with one-way valve**
3. Pan or 1000 ml beaker for boiling equipment
4. 100 ml beaker scored at 50 ml volume
5. 1.0 ml pipette
6. Hand lens or 10x microscope
7. Tongs
8. Forceps
9. Ampoule breaker**
10. Bunsen burner
11. Distilled water
12. MF-ENDO Medium Ampoules**
13. Filter pads**
14. Test Filters (Type HAWG)**
15. Plastic petri dishes**

** From Millipore.

*Courtesy of Millipore Corporation.

valve. Attach rubber hose to the side connecter of the one-way valve. Check other end of hose for presence of adaptor. Connect adaptor end of tubing to long side arm of receiving flask. Cap the short side arm of the flask.

7. Flame forceps and allow to cool. Remove a millipore filter pad from the sterile envelope. Raise the top edge of a petri dish, place the pad in the dish, and loosely close. (Use forceps to handle pad.)
8. Flame the end of an ampoule, break narrow end with ampoule breaker. Raise top edge of petri dish and pour growth media onto filter pad.

Sample Preparation

Procedure:

1. Remove funnel cover. Run distilled water to the 50 ml mark on the 100 ml beaker. Pour the distilled water into the funnel.
2. Pipette 1.0 ml of sample water into filter funnel and replace funnel cover.
3. Gently swirl to mix. Hold hand vacuum assembly firmly with left hand. Work plunger back and forth with right hand until sample is drawn through the filter. After vacuum is established, only occasional pumps are needed to maintain vacuum.
4. At completion of filtering process, remove funnel cover and rinse walls of funnel with another 50 ml of distilled water. Swirl and pull rinse water through funnel with hand vacuum assembly.
5. Flame and cool forceps. Unscrew funnel and remove filter from filter support with forceps. Raise one edge of petri dish top and carefully center filter on top of saturated pad. Replace petri dish top.
6. Invert petri dish and incubate at room temperature for 48 hours or at 37°C for 24 hours.

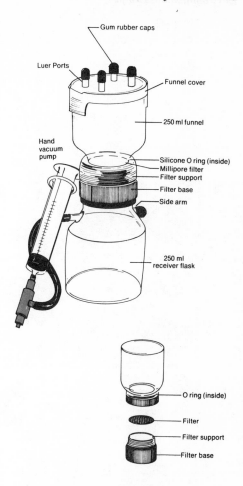

Figure 15-1 Millipore sterifil filtration apparatus. Detail from Figure 15-1.

COLONY COUNT

PROCEDURE:

1. At the end of the incubation period, remove filter from petri dish. Allow it to dry on clean blotter for $\frac{1}{2}$ hour.
2. Using a 10x power hand lens or microscope, count the colonies of bacteria which have a shiny green appearance. The green colonies represent the number of coliform bacteria that were present in the original sample. Other bacterial colonies will not produce a shiny green color. If the count exceeds 100 coliform colonies, water sample should be tested again using a smaller sample size (0.5 ml or 0.25 ml).
3. Coliform density is presented as the (total) coliforms per 100 ml, and may be determined using the following equation:

$$(\text{Total}) \text{ coliform colonies}/100 \text{ ml} = \frac{\text{coliform colonies counted} \times 100}{\text{ml sample filtered}}$$

TEST MECHANICS:

Coliform bacteria are unique in that they break down lactose (a sugar) into simple substances, including aldehydes.

The culture medium turns most colonies growing in the petri dish red. The aldehydes produced by the coliform bacteria react with the red dye of the medium to produce a shiny green color. No other bacteria produce this reaction, so coliform colonies are easily detected.

NOTE:

Local authorities should be consulted to find out what are acceptable coliform counts for potable water, raw water, public swimming pools, etc.

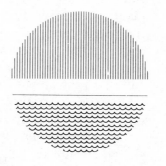

16. Terrestrial Biology

The following exercises are designed to illustrate concepts that pertain particularly to terrestrial communities, although many of the procedures may be applied to aquatic situations. A traditional means of evaluating terrestrial communities is the quadrat method. Quadrats are uniform areas marked off within particular plant communities.* Plant communities are associations of plant species that occur predictably over more or less large areas. (For example, a moss covered shelf along a stream bed

---

*Species composition of plant communities varies regionally. Almost any region has local keys, but these are usually restricted to particular kinds of environments such as deserts, marine coasts, chaparral, redwood forests, etc. Local keys are found by consulting libraries, nature-oriented groups, and College-University botany departments.

can be a plant community.) Quadrat size depends upon the goals of the study and the nature of the plant community.

Quadrats are studied intensively; then the results of the quadrat evaluation are projected to the part of the study area covered by that plant community. Each type of plant community will be different from the next in terms of variability. The same type of plant community found under different conditions may also have differences in species variability. Therefore, for each type another quadrat test should be conducted. In order to evaluate variable environments, more samples are necessary than when evaluating homogenous or less variable environments. This raises the question: What number of quadrats is necessary to produce a sample that adequately represents the community being studied? There should be enough quadrats to make a valid sample, and yet it is inefficient to sample more quadrats than are necessary. The probable best number of quadrats for each plant community can be determined from a species-area curve (Figure 16–1), in which the number of species sampled is plotted against the number of quadrats sampled. As the number of quadrats analyzed increases, the number of species collected also increases. Determination of an adequate number of quadrats for a representative sample is made by noting when the sampling of additional quadrats produces few or no additional species. This is represented on the species area curve plot by a flattening of the curve (Figure 16–1). An even, homogeneous environment will give a representative sample with few quadrats, while a heterogeneous habitat will require more quadrats to obtain a representative sample.

The number of quadrats necessary for a representative sample is used to determine the mean (average) number of individuals within each species. The number of quadrats is divided into the total number of individuals of a particular species for all quadrats. This estimate of species composition for one quadrat is then multiplied by the area of the plant community. For example, species counts within square-meter

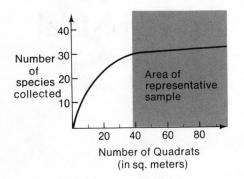

Figure 16–1 *Species Area Curve. Every environment will have a unique distribution of organisms. To find the number of quadrats necessary to constitute a representative sample of a particular environment, count the species collected as quadrat sampling proceeds. When determination of additional quadrats produces little or no increase in numbers of species collected (40 quadrats on the graph), the number of quadrats is adequate. Note that the curve "flattens" showing that increased sampling efforts will yield little increase in number of species. Determination of species proportions requires more sophisticated techniques.*

quadrats in a particular field, are continued until the curve of cumulative results plotted on a species-area curve levels out. Then the number of quadrats used (e.g., 15) is divided into the total counts (e.g., 150 mustard plants/15 quadrats = an average of 10 mustard plants per m² quadrat). If the field is 25 meters square (25 m × 25 m = 625 m²), the projected population of mustard plants is 625 m² × 10 plants/m² = 6,250 plants. For an analysis of a different community, such as that found in the field hedgerows, the procedure must be repeated including the tabulation of a species-area curve. Population data are often useful when considered together with other data from an area, such as soil analysis, history of planting of the field, and height of the field above the water table. Comparisons can be made between fields or a field can be divided into halves and fertilizer or other substances added to one half, then the development of the communities on each half studied.

Population distributions exist in time as well as space. The patterns of distribution over space can easily be recognized, but in the case of animals they may vary from one time of day to the next, or from one season to the next. Sampling of animals over time reveals patterns of movement that may relate to feeding, mating, overwintering, or other activities.

Population distributions over time can be determined by returning to an initial sampling station for additional sampling or observation. Important things to observe are variations in physical conditions, such as temperature, light, humidity, and nature of the substrate, as well as changes in vegetation and animal populations. There may be changes in the way that the animals are distributed over the habitat (compare clustered overwintering creatures with the evenly spaced individuals of a spawning population). Another difference may be a seasonal die-off. Some plants and animals are abundant during the growing season and scarce during unfavorable times of the year.

Complete note-taking is important. Significant conditions may not be evident until several past observations are available for comparison. For example, many animals move at dawn and dusk, stimulated by dim light. Such a pattern may not be obvious until a series of observations are compared. Variations shown by plant and animal populations can be documented through the use of map overlays, with distributions charted on each overlay.

Quadrat Sampling

Samples are taken through the use of a quadrat (usually a square meter, or some multiple) and then intensely studied. Plants and animals within the quadrat are counted, weighed or measured, and dominant species and other important data recorded, such as ground cover, size of trees, health of plants, or insect damage. While this technique lends itself well to terrestrial work, it can also serve to evaluate an aquatic environment with shallow substrate.

PROCEDURE:

1. Select a representative area of the habitat. It is important to avoid bias (bias is an influence that comes from outside the sample, usually resulting in error). Sources of bias are many, and often they are unconscious. For example, when searching for a representative area, an experimenter may feel that some trees should be in the sample area, even though trees are not a common thing in the region being sampled. The sample then would indicate more trees than were in the area. One way of avoiding bias is to take random samples. If several samples are in close agreement, the values are probably representative of the region. Methods of choosing random sample sites range from simply throwing a rock into the area (this method still may include some bias) to the virtually bias-free

method of gridding off the area on a map, numbering the grids, and selecting sample sites using a random number table from a statistics book.

2. Mark out a quadrat. Quadrat size depends upon type of foliage. Sizes should range from 1 meter square to 5 meters or more. A forest will require a larger quadrat than a close, shrub environment.
3. Drive a stake into the ground at each corner of the quadrat. Tie a tightly stretched string to the stakes, enclosing the sample area.
4. Depending upon the purpose of the study, count, measure, and identify material of concern in the quadrat. The small sample area allows time for a careful job. Note particular characteristics of the vegetation, such as ground cover, tree canopy, vegetation height and development, and condition (disease).
5. Stake out other quadrats and check for agreement of values. If counts between quadrats vary greatly, check for bias or other sources of error. To determine if there are adequate samples, a useful test is a species-area curve (Figure 16–1).
6. Use the most abundant species or a predominant feature of the vegetation to identify the plant community (a habitat type that seems consistent for large areas). It can be described, and then referred to using a dominant feature, such as *Manzanita*, sage, or serpentine rock.
7. Determine mean (average) quadrat values for each species, then multiply by the area (in m²) of the plant community under study (see introduction to this chapter for further information).

NOTE:

Another variation possible with quadrat sampling is a color slide photograph of the quadrat, projected on a sampling grid and then evaluated for ground cover.

In regions of close ground cover (e.g., grassland), where it is difficult to distinguish one plant from another or where damage to vegetation is to be avoided, the point frame method is useful. A frame with sharpened pins projecting downward at regular intervals is set on the terrain, and the first plants encountered by the points are recorded (Smith, 1966: 329).

Mapping

PROCEDURE:

1. Obtain, if possible, a large-scale map of the area. If such a map is not available, map the major landmarks of the area.
2. Using the landmarks as reference points, sketch in the boundaries of the plant community being studied.
3. The area of an irregularly shaped vegetational unit may be determined either by:
   a. Cut out a standard unit (1 m², 10 m²) of the paper being used, at the scale of the map. Using an analytical balance, weigh the standard unit (gives grams per standard unit), then weigh the irregular region under study.

   $$\frac{\text{weight of study region}}{\text{weight of standard unit}} = \text{area of study region in standard units}$$

   b. Trace the boundary of the study region with a planimeter (a mechanical device for measuring areas of shapes with irregular outlines) and read the area directly.
4. Map in the other vegetational units, paying close attention to the "edge" habitat between adjacent units. "Edgeness" is often very productive, and may hold plants and animals found in neither of the bordering units.

5. Refer to the information obtained from quadrat sampling for dominant, rare, and other forms in the unit. To find totals of a particular animal or plant population for the region being sampled, multiply the quadrat value (e.g., grasshoppers per m²) by the total area of the vegetational unit. For an estimate of the total weight of grasshoppers, multiply the weight of grasshoppers per m² by the area of the vegetational unit.

Another method of mapping, where landmarks may not be dramatic, is to pace off, at regular intervals (using compass bearings), stakes that can be laid down in a grid pattern. The stakes can then be used as orientation for finer map details. The result is a base map. Data from vegetation type, animal distribution, soil type, and other factors can be compared by making overlays to fit over the base map. The correlation between soil type, vegetation type, and animal distribution is often dramatic.

Sampling: Mark and Recapture

For evaluations of populations (i.e., the number of a single species of animal, as compared to the many species of a community) an interesting test, called mark and recapture, is used. Animals are captured, marked, and turned loose. Then members of the same population are recaptured and counted. The number of marked individuals (compared to unmarked) gives a clue as to the total number of animals in the population.

An estimate of the total population may be made according to the following equation — note assumptions required for validity.

Mark and Recapture Determinations

M_1 = Creatures marked
M_2 = Marked creatures recaptured on second collecting occasion
U = Unmarked creatures captured on second collecting occasion
P = Estimate of total population

$$\frac{M_1}{P} = \frac{M_2}{U} \qquad \text{or} \qquad P = \frac{(M_1)(U)}{M_2}$$

Assumptions necessary for this method to predict population size:

1. Mark must not affect behavior of the creature.
2. Sampling characteristics of the population must be the same for each collection (same time of day, same weather conditions, same collecting techniques may be necessary to assure similar conditions for recapture).
3. The population is distributed randomly throughout the habitat (a problem with territorial species).
4. There is no change in the population size between the two collection times.

Snail Populations

Land snails are easy to use in experiments with mark and recapture techniques for the evaluation of population size and movements.

PROCEDURE:

1. Locate vegetation suitable for snail populations, preferably a lawn surrounded by thick vegetation.
2. On a damp night, maximum numbers of snails will be moving. Count and mark each snail with quick-drying enamel, fingernail polish, etc.

3. The next damp evening, recapture and estimate the total population size using the mark and recapture formula.

Possible variations of the above experiment:

a. Code snails with different colors for different areas of the yard. Determine extent of movement.
b. During the day, search at base of shrubs, trees, fence posts, etc. for quiescent snails. Mark and check later for tendency to "home." Also check extent of movements around home base by coding different "nests" of snails with different colors.

SWEEPING

Sweeping is a good way to collect specimens quickly for mark and recapture studies. This technique works best with flying or hopping insects that rest on high portions of plants.

PROCEDURE:

1. Walk through the sample area, sweeping the vegetation with a long-handled, lightweight insect net.
2. Vary speed of the movement and portion of the vegetation sampled. The effectiveness of each variation may be determined by comparing recorded numbers of insects collected. Select the most effective method and start the marking procedure.
3. Mark each insect collected with a small drop of quick-drying enamel, fingernail polish, etc., and release.
4. Work through the vegetational unit or a predetermined sample area.
5. The next day, at the same time, repeat the sweeping action. Make at least as much effort as was expended in the first run for the same area. Numbers of insects collected should be the same or greater than in the first collection.

6. Count (marked and unmarked) individuals and estimate population size using the mark and recapture formula.

TRAPPING

Trapping of small mammals and particularly birds should be done with care. Permits are usually required. Extensive trapping can modify the ecology of an environment, usually for the worse. Except under supervision of the director of a banding or census program, collecting of birds is not recommended.

Mice are territorial animals and tend to distribute themselves evenly (non-randomly) throughout an environment. Because of this, they are subject to experimental bias. They also tend to learn the locations of live traps and come to them for food, particularly if the traps are less than 100% efficient. None the less, some interesting biology can be learned from mice. For example, under conditions of good weather and food supply, field mice live outside. When these conditions deteriorate, the field mice move into available dwellings, which puts them into competition with the resident house mice.

PROCEDURE:

1. Obtain several folding live traps.
2. Place seeds or a blob of peanut butter and a wad of cotton (so the mouse can survive temperature changes until released) in the far end of the trap and set it on a possible mouse runway. Field guides (Burt and Grossenheider, 1964) will serve to identify possible runways, habitats, and identification of specimens.
3. Check the traps at 12 hour intervals. Mark the mice by staining a small area of the fur with dye or a chemical stain.
4. Estimate population size, using mark and recapture formula.

COLLECTING AND TAGGING METHODS FOR
OTHER VERTEBRATE GROUPS

a. *Reptiles* — Collected lizards and turtles can be marked with non-toxic paint or by small notches in hard parts of the external anatomy.
b. *Fish* can be marked with tags, colored latex injected into fin rays, or selective clipping of fins. Collection can be by net, traps, or hook and line. Check with Fish and Game authorities before collecting or marking fish.
c. *Amphibians* can be tagged or clipped (toes or notches in fin webs).

Examination of Soil

Soil analysis is a rather specialized procedure. We believe that the most practical approach to soil analysis is to use a kit. The best soil testing kits for the money that we have seen are made by the LaMotte Chemical Company.

Soils are identified on the basis of particle size and organic content. Sand, silt, and clay are soil types identified, respectively, by decreasing size of the soil particles. Particle size and other properties are responsible for many characteristics of soil types such as the dense, sticky texture of clay soil. Loam is a soil type composed of roughly equal parts of the three size grades, usually including organic materials. Loam is the best category of soil for most plants. The organic portion of soil is termed humus. A soil that is largely organic matter, characterized by a dark color, and fibrous, spongy texture, is termed humus soil. With practice, basic soil types will be recognized by certain chemical and biological characteristics. Important factors in soil include nutrients (nitrates,

MATERIALS

1. Berlese funnel
   a. Light and heat source
   b. Funnel
   c. Fine-mesh hardware cloth
   d. Support
2. Collecting jar
3. Alcohol

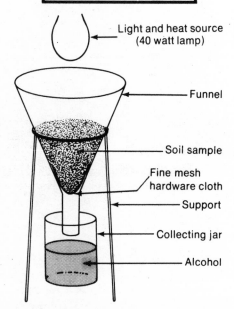

Light and heat source (40 watt lamp)

Funnel

Soil sample

Fine mesh hardware cloth

Support

Collecting jar

Alcohol

Figure 16-2 Berlese funnel. The light is suspended about four inches above the soil sample. First the heat and then dessication will drive the soil arthropods into the beaker of alcohol.

phosphates, potassium) and pH, as well as the biological elements which will often indicate the nature of the soil (Figure 16-3). For example, the plant *Salicornia* indicates saline soil.

PROCEDURE:

1. Because of the existence of various combinations of soils, it may be impossible to collect one of the five basic types. If this is the case, record the presence of intermediates, such as sandy loam, etc.
2. Bring to the lab at least enough of each soil type to fill a Berlese funnel. If some of the suggestions in Step 4 are to be tried, bring sufficient quantities of soil.
3. Determination of soil arthropods:
   a. Construct a facsimile of the Berlese funnel (Figure 16-2) for each soil test, if possible. If duplicate funnels are not available, keep the soil moist and protected until it can be tested.
   b. Put the soil in the funnel. The soil animals are driven out through the bottom of the funnel by the heating and drying effects of the light bulb. Collect the animals, count, and sort (Figure 16-3).
   c. Enter the results in a copy of Table 16-1. The characteristic fauna for the soil sample will then be indicated.
4. Other possible experiments:
   Divide several samples into two parts. Compare the control, which is not altered, to the experimental sample which will be modified. Differences between control and experimental, if all other conditions remain constant, will be due to the experimental treatment. Possible experiments include: shifting the pH by adding acid or base to the soil, turning the soil, growing particular plants, using different watering schedules, and using different food supplies. Allow time for the populations to equilibrate and check for the extent and kind of community changes.

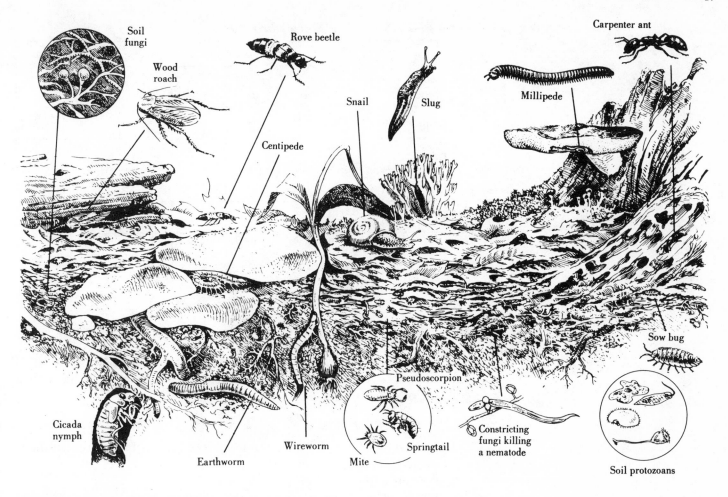

Figure 16–3 *Life in the soil. This drawing shows only a tiny fraction of the organisms that inhabit the soil and litter. Note the fruiting bodies of the fungi, which in turn furnish food for animals. (Figure 14–1 "Life in the Soil" page 262 from ECOLOGY AND FIELD BIOLOGY by Robert L. Smith. Copyright © 1966 by Robert L. Smith. Reprinted by permission of Harper & Row Publishers, Inc.)*

Table 16-1   Soil Type/Soil Arthropods

Soil Arthropods							
Soil type	a	b	c	d	e	f	g
Sand							
Loam							
Silt							
Clay							
Humus							

The Transect

The transect is a sampling technique that measures the abundance and kind of vegetation over a measured distance, usually through a gradient of habitat type.

PROCEDURE:

1. Drive two stakes into the ground at the limits of a desired gradient of environmental types.
2. Stretch a line between the two stakes and tie.
3. Every plant or sessile animal that the line (transect) passes over, under, or touches is to be recorded (see step 4). Different ways of recording the data can be used, including counting individual

plants, or estimating per cent of the ground cover, weight (biomass), or total individuals in a swath 6 inches on each side of the string. The swath method (belt transect) is also useful in observing the presence of animals within a transect. For animal transects, a wider swath is sometimes advisable.

4. It is instructive to make a table, such as that of Table 16–2, so that the gradient can be visualized. When the data are entered in such a table, gradients of habitat type and species are graphically indicated. Other data, such as measurements of physical and chemical conditions, can provide correlative information for the transect. In a shore transect or in similar gradients from unstable to stable conditions, a succession system can be illustrated. Early succession species will appear near the water's edge; later succession or climax communities will appear near the top of the gradient.

Table 16–2 *A Line Transect*

Species	Number of plants and sessile animals observed (or weight)						
A	5	3		1			
B		3	2		1		
C	7	5	4	3	2	1	
D			1	4	3	8	
E				1	4	6	10
F							30

Table 16–2 *Line transect indicating a river bank, grading into a woodland with increasing elevation and distance from the river.*

APPENDIX

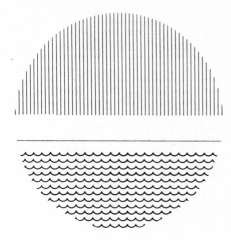

Provided with conceptual background and laboratory procedures, there are still a number of things to accomplish. Preparation of physical equipment and organization of activities are necessary, before the things that "look good on paper" can actually happen. This section provides some practical support to help assure that planned activities accomplish their goals.

Field Trips

It is nearly essential to have field trips to exemplify the concepts treated in readings, lectures, and laboratory. Field trips which explore large and typical environments will most graphically bring out basic principles. Often, such trips are not possible for a variety of reasons. Even when extended trips are planned, an alternative trip or laboratory exercise should be available if bad weather or some other unexpected event prevents the trip. There are still a number of interesting possibilities when a class is limited to local activities.

Without leaving the laboratory, a profile of physical (and sometimes biological!) conditions can be sketched from tap water. Data related to hardness, pH, alkalinity, etc. can stimulate discussion on the origin of the water and the kinds of substrate exposed to it. Discussions of water treatment can often lead to reservoir and purification plant field trips. Many interesting and constructive possibilities for further research are often suggested by coliform analysis of various water supplies. Tap water run through fine, silk bolting cloth (#20 or finer) has revealed plankton in some localities.

Instructive aquatic systems can be put together in the laboratory, within the confined spaces of aquaria, gallon jars, or other containers. An undisturbed container of tap water on a window sill will begin to show biological succession within a few days. Water quality measurements taken at regular intervals can illustrate the interaction between biological and physical elements. Regular estimations of species abundance, made with the Sedgwick-Rafter technique, can demonstrate succession when plotted against the age of the culture in days. As new organisms appear, flourish, and then fade, they will be recorded on the chart. The physical correlates to the behavior of plankton populations suggest hypotheses and encourage further tests, such as culturing, to verify those explanations. Succession in an aquarium filled with tap water can be compared to succession in an aquarium seeded with grass cuttings. The differences in plant and animal communities may demonstrate the contrast between rich and sterile aquatic environments. Drawings or photographs of typical organisms can be assembled and related to the communities being studied. Such a study may be the nucleus of several group projects.

Most of the exercises designed for large bodies of water can be done in miniature, using an aquarium. An environmental profile can be assembled. Natural situations can be simulated by matching dilutions. For example, the effects of 500 vacationing families on a lake can be simulated by developing a proportion and then diluting equivalent amounts of waste water in an aquarium. Controlled quantities of pesticides, nutrient pollution of various types, and chemical contamination, such as oil, can also be dumped into a "simulated lake" aquarium. To show the effects of shallow beaches or bays, models can be made from clay or plaster of paris. The artificial effluent will be concentrated in such areas when circulation is poor.

Other sources of study include mud puddles, which can show that interesting biological communities exist in the most humble places. Mud puddles are especially valuable because some of the principles of lake biology apply to them. The use of mud puddles as lake models and the determination of disparities between puddles and the lakes helps to illustrate the physical requirements for phenomena, such as stable thermal layering.

Irrigation and drainage ditches are normally a rich source of plankton. Depending upon permanence of the water in the ditch, there may be other aquatic animals, such as fish and amphibians. Ditches are one of the best places to look for muskrats. Check with local authorities before collecting.

Municipal sewage treatment plants are an often overlooked but instructive field trip. Treatment plants have always been of interest to biologists for their demonstration of the decomposer level of community structure. Visits to such plants are now of more general concern. Nutrient overloads of streams and other water resources result in eutrophication, oxygen depletion, and other problems. Personnel of the plants are usually very cooperative in demonstrating and explaining these and other kinds of problems, and in discussing the workings and limitations of such plants. Visitors are usually surprised at the complexity of waste treatment and disposal. Also worth considering are individual aspects of the treatment plant, such as communities on rocks of trickling filters, oxidation ponds, and the digestors with their parallel to natural systems. Methane gas generated from sewage sludge digestion can be and is often used to run the engines for the sludge pumps.

Field Trip Planning

The success of a field trip rests upon planning and organization. Students sent into the field unfamiliar with equipment, data collecting, and purpose are not likely to achieve the intended purpose of the activity. Further, in many instances, they may do substantial harm to an environment. There are still teachers who allow their students to take "just two" animals from a seashore field trip. The students following such instructions usually end up with a viscous mass in their peanut butter jars, which goes into the garbage disposal shortly after they arrive home. The intertidal community in parts of California has become so reduced by such abuse that collecting has been banned completely throughout the state. It is the instructor's responsibility to investigate the nature of the environment and to insure that his field trip will not cause damage. Apparently harmless acts may have large consequences. For example, walking on small delicate Alpine plants may kill years of growth. If precautions are not observed, regulatory agencies will justifiably restrict the use of natural resources as they have done in California.

Field trip planning should be carefully organized, but the trip itself need not be rigidly structured. In this way the discipline of the scientific approach is not lost, yet the student is allowed personal latitude.

Specific preparations for field trips should include demonstrations (ideally, actual practice) using field equipment. It is valuable to include students in pre- and post-trip inventory, packing, and checking of equipment and supplies. Student involvement is enhanced when everyone participates in all aspects of the trip. It is not doing a student a service to train him to expect the equipment to appear when needed. At a pre-trip meeting, the field trip group should be divided into teams, each team specializing in one test or aspect of the trip. Team responsibility should rotate from one trip to the next, and the teams should be encouraged to consult with each other for greater appreciation of the accomplishments of the trip. The mechanical aspects of the trip should be decided well in advance and a description should be distributed to the group with a synopsis of general background information about the field trip site. Such a "handout" should include meeting places (with maps if necessary), times, meal arrangements, facilities, and personal equipment needed. Information that will enhance the value of the trip includes geological history, presence of fossils, nearby exhibits or museums, and other background materials that have been assembled.

When the group arrives at the field trip site, individuals or teams should spend the morning collecting data and running their assigned tests. If the students know what they are going to do, they can get started immediately. A trip that begins with a minimum of confusion is off to a good start.

There should be a definite break for lunch together; otherwise the group effort will fragment. Informal conversations about progress, and additional ideas for the afternoon's work help to generate cross-team interest. At another specific time in the afternoon the group should meet again, and each team should make a presentation based on the day's work. Individual data, as well as important data presented from other groups, should be entered in each student's field notebook at this time. The group should be encouraged to assemble the data in such a way that a perspective for the total environment can be assembled (i.e., environmental profile, Chap. 14).

Model for a Class Field Trip

The following is provided as a possible sketch of some class activities for a one-day field trip:

Class size — 20
Field trip — to small shallow lake

Equipment used may include:

Topographic map of field trip area
Area maps (i.e., road map, city, county maps)
Microscopes
   Compound
   Binocular (dissecting)
Buckets
Specimen jars and vials
Formalin
BOD bottles and rack

Rubber raft or car top boat* (plus safety equipment — floats, etc.)
Kemmerer Sampler
Plankton nets (2)
Sedgwick-Rafter Counting Cell
Water Quality Kit including tests for DO, CO_2, pH, hardness, coliform
Foot-operated corer, with screens
Secchi Disc

---

* If no boat is available, you can use a bridge, dam face, or steep shore slope.

Thermometers (each student should have a pocket thermometer)
Sounding line or fish locator

Small seine
References
$\frac{1}{2}$ meter quadrat
Soil Kit

A. PRE-TRIP PREPARATION (on a day prior to the trip)

  a. Assemble the gear, and go over it with the class. If possible, walk to a nearby water source to demonstrate.

  b. Divide the class into teams. For example:

Plankton Crew	4 students
Water Quality Crew	4 students
Seining Crew	4 students
Benthos Crew	4 students
Physical Conditions	4 students

B. TENTATIVE FIELD TRIP PLAN

A workable timetable for a field trip is: on the site by 8:00 or 9:00 A.M., leave the site to be home by 5:00 P.M. This allows for an early start in the field, yet gets the group back at a reasonable hour.

  1. Early Boat Run: 2 to 4 students (representatives from plankton crew, physical conditions crew, water quality crew) take Kemmerer samples through the water column.

    a. Use water from Kemmerer to determine temperature at 5 meter increments, then at 1 meter near the thermocline (Chap. 3).

    b. Strain same water through plankton net; set aside for later analysis by plankton crew.

    c. Record the temperature profile and location of thermocline.

      d. Take Kemmerer samples at depth intervals similar to those for the temperature profile. Add the first two chemicals for oxygen analysis; set aside for later analysis. From early boat run: plankton, oxygen, and temperature data are obtained for the water column (surface to below thermocline). Return to shore: plankton and oxygen to proper crews for analysis.

2. Boat is free to:
      a. Tow for large plankton samples to determine species diversity, and to sample various areas of the water for clumping distribution of plankton.
      b. Physical conditions: explore the bottom configuration by sounding or by portable fish locator.
      c. Explore the shore configuration where not accessible from shore.

3. Other morning activities:
      a. Plankton crew: set up microscopes in protected area, sample surface and nearshore water for plankton, and analyze. Begin analysis of plankton when boat comes in. Rotate crew: 2 counting, 2 collecting.
      b. Water quality crew: half on boat, half analyzing surface waters from nearshore areas. Rotate crew — 2 collecting, 2 counting.
      c. Seining crew: 2 on net, 1 carrying plastic container for specimens, 1 taking field notes (temperature, locations, directions, and results of hauls). Rotate responsibilities.
      d. Benthos crew: 4 set up quadrat, then 2 continue on quadrat, and 2 begin mapping of shore bottom (substrate, benthic communities). Pairs rotate at intervals.
      e. Physical conditions crew: must have map ready at start of

trip. 2 identify and roughly map basic soil conditions and dominant vegetation. 2 sound lake contour and draw depth contours.

4. Lunch and discussion. Time 12:00 noon.
5. Recap morning's work (12:00–1:30).
6. Afternoon: finish up, follow up suggestions from recap session (1:30 to departure time). Allow one hour before departure to write field notes and pack gear (time depends on travel time necessary to reach home by 5:00).
7. Class results expected at end of trip:
   a. All students: notes of day's activities (personal as well as general results of group efforts).
   b. Plankton crew: counts and identification of plankton, comparing surface, shore, and below thermocline. Nature of distribution (patchiness). Epiphyton (plankton on substrate).
   c. Water quality crew: dissolved oxygen, carbon dioxide, pH, hardness, and coliform for surface and shore (compare various areas, particularly with respect to coliform) and below thermocline.
   d. Seining crew: species and relative abundance of fish, amphibia, and large invertebrates. Map locations of capture, estimates of size, and weight of specimens examined.
   e. Benthos crew: description of basic types of benthic communities present. Maps of types of substrate and communities of nearshore bottom areas.
   f. Physical conditions crew: start with map of drainage basin. Rough map of soil types and dominant vegetational types present. Map of lake bottom contours.

Care and Storage of Equipment

Field equipment is variable in accuracy, ruggedness, and susceptibility to error. Before using equipment, it is important to learn the idiosyncrasies of each item. Sensitive equipment, such as oxygen probes or thermistors (electronic thermometers), should have priority for safe places (in car or boat) over tough equipment, such as most water samplers, dredges, cores, secchi discs, etc.

Corrosive or toxic chemicals, such as formalin, should be packed in sturdy plastic containers (never glass) and stored in an area away from equipment that might be damaged by leakage. The following precautions should be observed: sunlight deteriorates rubber and nylon, is hard on electronic equipment, and will reduce the usable life of most chemicals. Nylon nets can be stored wet. This is preferable to long periods of drying in the sun. Cotton or hemp lines and netting should be dried before storage. Whenever possible, equipment items, particularly small objects such as vials, forceps, clamps, and the like, should have handy storage places. For routine work a section of 2 × 4 lumber, drilled with a series of holes slightly larger than the commonly used articles, keeps them handy until needed and provides a means of checklisting the equipment.

Equipment should be washed, dried, and stored as part of the field trip. For example, the rubber end stoppers of Kemmerer Samplers form grooves and will leak if stored in the closed position. Spring-loaded dredges should have springs in a relaxed position for storage.

Equipment should be routinely checked for proper operation before and after use. Loss of equipment (e.g., nets lost due to parted lines) can almost always be avoided through this practice. Whenever possible, it is desirable to carry spare parts and replacement items for vulnerable equipment. The cost of a spare water sampler is relatively small compared to the expense of a class traveling to a field trip site.

Field Notes and Collection Data

On a field trip many things are usually going on at once. It is easy to get the impression that any notes taken will be inadequate. For this reason, it is important for each individual to concentrate on one aspect of the situation, and to take no more data than can be carefully and accurately recorded. It is also very useful to learn to write observations down immediately. In the midst of some interesting or busy observation, there is a natural tendency to rely on memory. Possible pertinent facts that do not seem important at the time will not be incorporated in notes written later. A standardized note-taking procedure will pay off in unexpected ways. For example, correlations of temperature or depth with reproductive behavior may not be obvious until notes from several observation periods are compared.

A hard-cover ring binder is recommended for a field notebook. Notes should be written with a soft lead pencil or preferably with permanent (India) ink on high rag-content paper. Notes taken this way are less vulnerable to accidental loss or damage. A notebook's value is greatly increased if there are no rules restricting the kinds of information to be recorded. Personal reflections, ideas, maps, and phonic attempts at sound description should be included with no reservations. Field notes should not be recopied. Time should be spent in rereading past notes, with constant attention to making the note-taking process more efficient. That is, with practice the notes should say more with less effort. Codes, abbreviations, and other devices are useful, but a key to any personal shortcuts should be included somewhere in the notebook.

When many kinds of data are to be recorded, such as water temperature, hardness, pH, clarity, dissolved oxygen, etc., it is handy to use a standard field note page; narrative notes can then be added. An example of such a page of field notes is presented in Figure A–1.

Survey __CALIFORNIA__
Drainage __SACRAMENTO RIVER__ Col. No. __WMK 72-23__
Locality __UPPER BLUE LAKE, 100 yd FROM STATE HWY 20, 2mi__
__N Jct. ST. HWY 29, S.E. SHORE NEAR BEACH__
County __LAKE__ Quadrangle __COW MOUNTAIN__ Elevation __1300'__
Water __QUIET, STRATIFIED__ Flow _____ Width __100 m__
Vegetation __PLANKTON, RICH ROOTED AQUATIC ELODEA,__

Bottom __SAND → SILT, MUD__ Current __NA__
Shore __BEACH TO WOODS__ Distance from shore _____
Temperature: Air __20° C__ Water __19/11°__ Time __1030__ Weather __SUN/CLEAR__
Depth of Capture __1-5 m__ Depth of Water __to 16 m__
Method of Capture __OBSERVATION__ Date __AUG 30, 1972__
Collected by __KAILL, FREY, JEROME HARGRAVES__
Orig. preserve _____ Time _____
pH _____
Clarity (secchi) __3m (S)__
Hardness __120 ppm (S)__
CO_2 __5 ppm (S)__
D.O. __8 ppm (S)__
Color __GREEN-BLUE (S)__ __GREY-GREEN BELOW__
                                          (CONT'D OVER)
General notes:

observation made with SCUBA
   S = SURFACE

PLANKTON VISIBLY LAYERED A FEW cm. ABOVE
"COLD" LAYER OF THERMOCLINE 10m DEEP

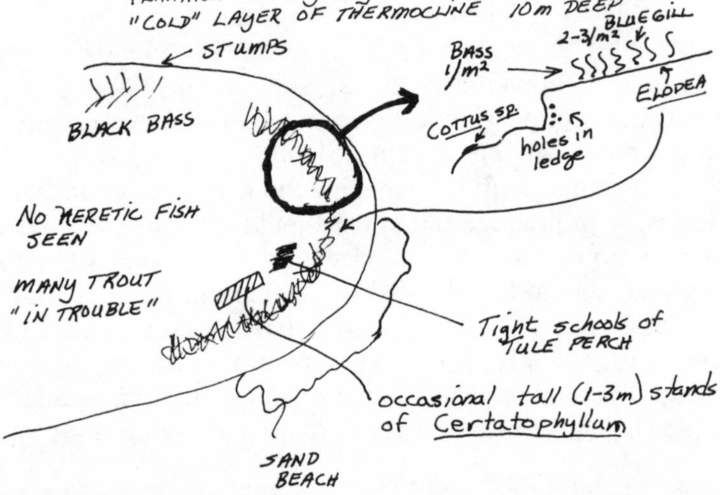

Figure A-1   Example of Field Note Page.

Water Samplers

Kemmerer Sampler

The Kemmerer Sampler* (Figure A–2) is a cylinder, open at both ends in the "cocked" position before it is triggered. Before taking each water sample, the sampler should be cocked open by pulling the upper and lower stoppers in opposite directions (away from the open ends of the tube) until a click is heard. The sampler will then hang in the open position, suspended by the line, until triggered. The sampler is lowered into the water until measurements marked on the line indicate the desired depth. The tubular structure of the Kemmerer, as well as that of other samplers such as the Van Dorn, allows water to pass through the core of the tube. Water in the tube is thus representative of the depth position of the sampler. When the Kemmerer Sampler is at the desired depth, a messenger is released, which slides down the supporting line and strikes the releasing mechanism, closing the sampler. (Occasionally, it is convenient to use the sampler from a bridge. If this is done, the messenger has greater force and will eventually damage the sampler unless a lighter weight "bridge" messenger is used.) When the Kemmerer is brought to the surface, the water is transferred into a sample bottle. The length of rubber hose attached to a "push" valve is inserted to the bottom of the sample bottle. The bottle is filled until it overflows, assuring a water sample uncontaminated by air.

Hach Sampler

This device is a small-capacity sampler, designed primarily for use in shallow water. It differs from most samplers (which are variations of

---

Popular Science recently published directions for the construction of a Kemmerer Sampler (Rakoff, 1972).

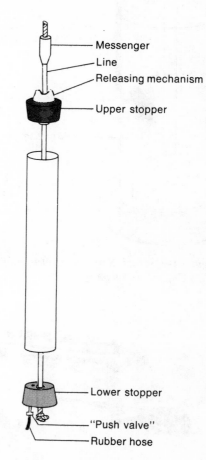

Figure A–2 Kemmerer Sampler.

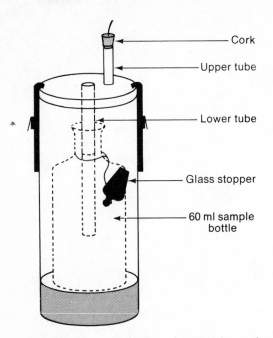

Cork

Upper tube

Lower tube

Glass stopper

60 ml sample
bottle

Figure A-3 Hach Sampler (Courtesy of
Hach Chemical Company).

the cylinder shape) in that the sample bottle is held inside the cup-shaped sampler (Figure A-3). Two tubes are incorporated into the lid of the sampler. One tube, flush with the surface of the sampler cap, serves as the water intake. The other tube, which extends above the cap, allows air to escape. When the sampler is ready for operation, the upper tube is corked. The air cannot escape out the blocked tube, which prevents water from entering the lower tube. The sampler is lowered into the water by a chain, and a long string leads from the cork to the experimenter. When the sampler reaches the required depth, the experimenter pulls out the cork. The water flows into the sampler through the lower tube, and fills the sample bottle from the bottom. The sampler overflows several times the sample bottle volume. The Hach sampler fills the sample bottle at the same time that it takes the sample. Other water sampler procedures (Kemmerer, etc.), fill and overflow the sample bottle (to avoid air contamination) as a separate procedure after the sample is brought to the surface. When the sampler comes up, the sample bottle is submerged inside the cup. Once the glass stopper is inserted into the sample bottle, the intact sample can be lifted out.

Other variations of the Kemmerer cylinder design are the Nansen Sampler and the Alpha Bottle (Figure A-4). If dissolved gas determina-

Figure A-4 Nansen Sampler and Alpha
Bottle (Courtesy of Wildlife Supply Company).

tions are not important, any container can serve as a sampler. Clean jars, cans, and bottles are all adequate for collecting surface water samples for hardness, plankton, pH, etc.

Preparation of Materials for Ecology Laboratory

CHAPTER 3: THERMOCLINE DETERMINATION

MATERIALS:

1. Thermometer
2. Water sampler

CHAPTER 4: TURBIDITY AND VISIBILITY

Secchi Disc Transparency

MATERIALS:

1. Secchi disc
2. Line marked in inches or centimeters. A secchi disc (Figure A–5a), constructed of wood or metal, is 20 cm in diameter. A bolt (machine screw eye) is threaded through the disc and into a threaded weight or nut on the underside of the disc (Figure A–5b, c). The weight

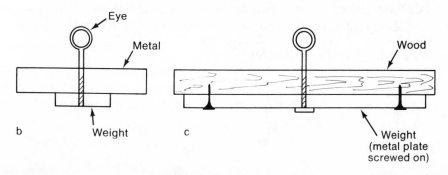

Figure A–5 *Secchi Disc showing details of construction. Alternating quarters are painted glossy jet black and white.*

maintains orientation of the disc. The upper surface is divided into four quarters. Alternating sections are painted glossy jet black and white. The premeasured line is attached to the eye on the upper surface.

Colorimeter

MATERIALS:

1. Colorimeter (Figure A–6)

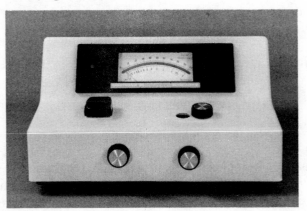

Figure A–6 Spectrophotometer (Courtesy of Bausch and Lomb).

2. Colorimeter tubes
   Colorimeters contain specific instructions for the test. If a spectrophotometer is available, it can be calibrated using standards.

Jackson Candle Turbidimeter

MATERIALS:

1. A tripod base which supports one standard candle exactly 7.6 cm or 3 in. from the base of the glass cylinder tube.

2. The candle is installed in a spring-loaded device to keep 7.6 cm distance.
3. Glass tubes with flat, polished bases, graduated to read turbidity in Jackson Turbidity Units.
4. Standard candle constructed to burn at a constant rate (Figure A–7).

Chapter 5: Chloride Ion Test (Burette Titration Method)

Step 1   pH Check

MATERIALS:

1. Wide-range pH paper
2. Solutions (in dropper bottles):
   a. *Sodium hydroxide, 1 N:*
      same as sodium hydroxide (NaOH), stock solution in carbon dioxide test materials, steps 2 & 3.
   b. *Sulfuric acid, 1 N:*
      same as sulfuric acid (H_2SO_4), stock solution in alkalinity test materials, step 3.

Step 2   Standardization of Silver Nitrate Titrant

MATERIALS:

1. 100 ml Erlenmeyer flask
2. 50 ml graduated cylinder
3. 50 ml burette, stand, and clamp for silver nitrate titration
4. 1.0 ml pipette
5. Solutions:
   a. *Standard sodium chloride, 0.0141 N:*
      Dissolve 824.1 milligrams of sodium chloride (NaCl) (dried at

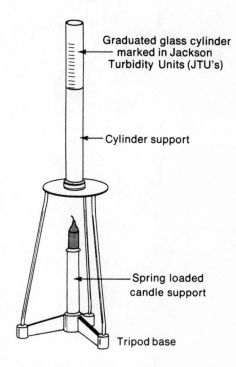

Graduated glass cylinder marked in Jackson Turbidity Units (JTU's)

Cylinder support

Spring loaded candle support

Tripod base

Figure A–7 Jackson Candle Turbidimeter.

140°F) in 200 ml of chloride-free water.* Dilute to one liter using chloride-free water.*

b. *Standard silver nitrate titrant, 0.0141 N:*
Dissolve 2.395 g of silver nitrate ($AgNO_3$) in 200 ml of distilled water. Dilute to one liter. Store in brown bottle in the dark.

c. *Potassium chromate indicator:*
Dissolve 50 g of potassium chromate (K_2CrO_4) in 500 ml of distilled water. Add 0.0141 N silver nitrate ($AgNO_3$) solution until a red precipitate is formed. Let stand overnight, filter, and dilute the solution to one liter with distilled water.

Step 3   Titration of Water Sample

MATERIALS:

1. 250 ml Erlenmeyer flask scored at 100 ml volume
2. 50 ml burette, stand, and clamp for silver nitrate titration
3. 1.0 ml pipette
4. Solutions:
Same as Step 2 except omit NaCl solution.

CHAPTER 6:   FREE CARBON DIOXIDE TEST

MATERIALS FOR BURETTE METHOD:

1. Water sampler
2. Thermometer
3. 250 ml Erlenmeyer flask scored at 100 ml volume
4. Burette, stand, and clamp for sodium hydroxide titration

MATERIALS FOR FIELD USE:

1. Water sampler

---

* Redistilled, or high-quality distilled water.

2. Thermometer
3. 100 ml Erlenmeyer flask scored at 50 ml volume
4. Plastic dropper bottle for sodium hydroxide (15 drops/ml)

SOLUTIONS:

1. *Phenolphthalein indicator:*
   There are two kinds of phenolphthalein indicator preparations:
   (a) water soluble, and (b) alcohol soluble.
   a. Dissolve 5 g of phenolphthalein disodium salt in 200 ml of distilled water.* Dilute to 1 liter with distilled water.*
   b. Dissolve 5 g of phenolphthalein in 500 ml of ethyl alcohol (or isopropyl alcohol). Dilute with 500 ml of distilled water.* Add drops of 0.02 N NaOH until a faint pink color appears (to eliminate acidification of indicator).

2. *Sodium hydroxide, stock solution, 15 N:***
   Completely dissolve 454 g NaOH in 650 ml distilled water.* (May take 48 hours to dissolve.) Caution: Highly corrosive.

3. *Sodium hydroxide, stock solution, 1 N:***
   Dilute 66.6 ml of 15 N NaOH solution to 1 liter with distilled water.*

4. *Sodium hydroxide, standard titrant, 0.0227 N*** (*working solution for burette method*):
   Dilute 22.7 ml of 1 N NaOH to 1 liter with distilled water.*

5. *Sodium hydroxide, 0.0171 N*** (*working solution for field method*):
   Dilute 17.1 ml of 1 N NaOH to 1 liter with distilled water.*

6. *Sodium hydroxide, 0.02 N* (*to neutralize phenolphthalein*):
   Dilute 20.0 ml of 1 N NaOH to 1 liter with distilled water.*

---

*The distilled water should be boiled for at least 10 minutes before use to eliminate any carbon dioxide (CO_2) and then cooled to room temperature before use.
**Store in polyethylene containers.

NOTES:

1. If other sample sizes are used, one may calculate the ppm using an equation found in *Standard Methods,* 1971:

$$\text{ppm of } CO_2 = \frac{A \times N \times 44{,}000}{\text{ml of sample}}$$

A = ml titration for sample.   N = normality of NaOH.

2. For information on color standards see *Standard Methods,* 1971: 93.

CHAPTER 6: pH TESTS

A. *Colorimetric Determination Methods*

pH Paper

MATERIALS:

1. Set of wide-range pH paper
2. Set of narrow-range pH paper
   (If paper is old, scratch surface with fingernail to improve accuracy.)

Color Comparator

MATERIALS:

1. Color comparator
2. Sample tubes
3. Indicator solutions
   Indicators are difficult to prepare. Convenience, low cost, and storage characteristics of commercially available indicators and indicator combinations recommend them over home preparation.

pH by Colorimetry

MATERIALS:

1. Colorimeter
2. Colorimeter tubes
3. Wide-range indicator solution
4. pH scale or calibration curve
5. Filter

B. Electrometric Determination Method

MATERIALS:

1. pH meter
2. Electrodes
   Adequate meters are expensive ($400–$1000). Each company supplies specific operating instructions. Inexpensive meters are normally a poor investment.

CHAPTER 6: ALKALINITY TESTS

MATERIALS FOR BURETTE METHOD:

1. 250 ml Erlenmeyer flask scored at 100 ml volume
2. Burette, stand, and clamp for sulfuric acid titration

MATERIALS FOR FIELD USE:

1. 100 ml Erlenmeyer flask scored at 50 ml volume
2. Dropper bottles for indicators and sulfuric acid (15 drops/ml)

SOLUTIONS:

1. *Phenolphthalein indicator:*
   Same as phenolphthalein solution in CO_2 test materials, step 1.

2. *Methyl Orange indicator:*
   Add to distilled water, 0.5 g high-quality methyl orange indicator.
   Dilute to 1.0 liter.
   Store in dark bottle.
3. *Sulfuric acid, stock solution, 1 N:*
   Dilute 22.7 ml of concentrated sulfuric acid (36 N) to 1.0 liter
   with distilled water. NOTE: Add acid to about 500 ml of distilled
   water before diluting solution to 1.0 liter. This is necessary to avoid
   spattering concentrated acid.
4. *Sulfuric acid, standard titrant, 0.02 N (working solution for burette method)*:
   Dilute 20.0 ml of 1 N stock solution to 1.0 liter with distilled water.
5. *Sulfuric acid, 0.075 N (working solution for field method)*:
   Dilute 75 ml of 1 N stock solution to 1.0 liter with distilled water.

CHAPTER 6:   TOTAL HARDNESS

MATERIALS:

1. 10 ml pipette
2. 100 ml beaker
3. Solutions (in dropper bottles: 15 drops/ml):
   a. Buffer solution
   b. Indicator
   c. EDTA* reagent or prepared mixture

The hardness test reagents are judged to be difficult enough in
preparation to exceed the capabilities of most laboratories. Persons
wishing to prepare their own chemical are directed to *Standard Methods*,
EDTA titrimetric method. Prepared and stable reagents for this test are

---

*Disodium dihydrogen ethylenediamine tetraacetate.

available from water testing companies or, less expensively, from biological and chemical supply companies.

CHAPTER 7: DISSOLVED OXYGEN TESTS

Winkler: Azide Modification

MATERIALS:

1. Water sampler
2. Thermometer
3. 300 ml BOD bottle or equivalent
4. Burette for sulfuric acid
5. 500 ml Erlenmeyer flask
6. Burette, stand, and clamp for sodium thiosulfate titration

SOLUTIONS:

1. *Manganous sulfate solution:*
   Dissolve 480 g of manganous sulfate ($MnSO_4 \cdot 4H_2O$) in distilled water. Dilute to one liter.
2. *Alkali-Iodide-Azide reagent (AIA):*
   a. Add to distilled water:
      1. 500 g sodium hydroxide (NaOH)
         (or 700 g potassium hydroxide, KOH)
      2. 135 g sodium iodide (NaI)
         (or 150 g potassium iodide, KI)
      3. Dilute this solution to 1.0 liter.
   b. To 40 ml of distilled water, add 10 g sodium azide (NaN_3).
   c. Mix the two solutions.
3. *Sulfuric acid, concentrated, 36 N*
4. *Starch solution:*
   a. Grind 10 g of soluble starch in a small amount of distilled water.

b. Add this solution to 1.0 liter of boiling water and boil for a few minutes.
c. Let stand overnight.
d. Use the clear supernatant solution. This solution may be preserved by adding 5 ml of chloroform for each liter of solution, and should be stored in a refrigerator.
e. "Thyodene," a dry, powdered starch indicator, may be used in place of the starch solution.

5. *Sodium thiosulfate, stock solution, 0.75 N:*
   a. In boiled and cooled distilled water, dissolve 186.15 g sodium thiosulfate ($Na_2S_2O_3 \cdot 5H_2O$).
   b. Make to 1.0 liter.
   c. Preserve with 5 ml of chloroform and store in a refrigerator.

6. *Sodium thiosulfate, standard titrant, 0.0375 N:*
   a. Dilute 50 ml of stock solution to 1.0 liter.
   b. Preserve by adding 5 ml of chloroform.
   c. Standardize with 0.0375 N potassium biiodate.

7. *Potassium biiodate standard, 0.0375 N:*
   a. Dry 5 g of potassium biiodate for 2 hours at 103°C.
   b. Dissolve 4.873 g of this material in 1.0 liter of distilled water.
   c. Dilute 250 ml to 1.0 liter for a 0.0375 N biiodate solution.

8. *Standardization of 0.0375 N sodium thiosulfate:*
   a. Dissolve about 2 g of KI in 100–150 ml of distilled water.
   b. Add 10 ml of 10% H_2SO_4 (1 part of H_2SO_4 to 9 parts of distilled water) and 20 ml of 0.0375 N potassium biiodate.
   c. Place in the dark for a few minutes.
   d. Dilute the solution to 300 ml with distilled water.
   e. Titrate with thiosulfate to a pale straw color.
   f. Add 1–2 ml of starch solution.
   g. Continue titrating until the blue color disappears.
   h. The amount of thiosulfate used should agree with the 20 ml of potassium biiodate to within ±0.05 ml.

i. This standardization should be run in duplicate.

Field Method: Hach

MATERIALS:*

1. Hach or other water sampler
2. 60 ml DO bottle
3. Calibrated measuring tube (5.8 ml)
4. Mixing bottle
5. Reagents:
    a. Dissolved Oxygen I (Manganous sulfate)
    b. Dissolved Oxygen II (Alkaline-Iodide-Azide)
    c. Dissolved Oxygen III (Dry Acid)
    d. PAO (Phenylarsene oxide)

Field Method: LaMotte

MATERIALS:**

1. Water sampler
2. Plastic sample bottle
3. 50 ml Erlenmeyer flask
4. Microburette
5. Droppers
6. Solutions:
    a. Manganese sulfate
    b. Alkaline potassium iodide
    c. Sulfuric acid
    d. Starch solution
    e. Sodium thiosulfate

---

*Available from Hach Chemical Company.

**Available from LaMotte Chemical Company.

Chapter 8: Biochemical Oxygen Demand (BOD)

MATERIALS:

1. Water sampler
2. Two 300 ml BOD bottles
3. Incubator or equivalent conditions
4. Materials for Dissolved Oxygen Determination (Chap. 7)

Chapter 11:   Plankton Sampling

All or some of the following may be needed depending on the procedure chosen for sampling and analysis.

Field Techniques

MATERIALS:

1. Phytoplankton net—No. 20 silk bolting cloth* (173 meshes per inch)
2. Towline
3. Collecting bottles in rack
4. Formalin
   40% Formaldehyde solution = 100% formalin. Formalin to be diluted to 4% solution.
5. Glycerin
   1 to 2 drops per 100 ml of 4% formalin
6. Boat, motor, or equivalent means of towing. Holding the net in a stream is equivalent to towing.
7. Thermometer
8. Water sampler

---

*Directions for Plankton Net Construction, see Welch, 1948: 232–236.

Laboratory Techniques

MATERIALS:

1. Microscope with micrometer or mechanical stage
2. Plankton key
3. Sedgwick-Rafter counting cell with cover slip
4. 1.0 ml calibrated eyedropper

CHAPTER 12: COLLECTION OF FISH: SEINE METHOD

MATERIALS:

1. Seine (Figure 12-1)
2. Two 6 ft. poles
3. Collecting pail with lid
4. Large pans or buckets

CHAPTER 15: TOTAL COLIFORM BACTERIA (MILLIPORE METHOD)

MATERIALS:

1. Millipore Sterifil Filtration Apparatus* (Figure 15-1)
2. Rubber hose and hand vacuum assembly with one-way valve.*
   (A side arm flask and an aspirator may also be used.)
3. Pan or 1000 ml beaker for boiling equipment
4. 100 ml beaker scored at 50 ml volume
5. 1.0 ml pipette
6. Hand lens or 10x microscope
7. Tongs
8. Forceps
9. Ampoule breaker*

---

*Available from Millipore Corporation.

10. Bunsen burner, wire gauze, and ring stand or hot plate
11. Distilled water
12. MF-ENDO Medium Ampoules*
13. Filter pads*
14. Test Filters (Type HAWG)*
15. Plastic (disposable) petri dishes*

Millipore Experiments in Environmental Microbiology, a pamphlet produced by the Millipore Corporation, is available upon request. Catalog No. LTPB 071 BB, Millipore Corporation, Bedford, Mass., 01730.

CHAPTER 16:   EXAMINATION OF SOIL

MATERIALS:

1. Berlese Funnel (Figure 16–2)
   a. Light and heat source
   b. Funnel
   c. Fine-mesh hardware cloth
   d. Support
2. Collecting jar
3. Alcohol

Equipment and Supply Sources

The following companies are a sampling of material sources for Part II. Persons interested in establishing contacts with suppliers are urged to scan the advertisements in civil engineering journals, newsletters, and journals such as *Industrial Research, Bioscience, Science,* and *American Biology Teacher.* Other examples of sources of information are provided at the end of this sec-

---

*Available from Millipore Corporation.

tion. Product newsletters and catalogs are constantly sent to university and college biology departments, and may also serve as sources of information.

Aloe Scientific
1831 Olive St.
St. Louis, Mo. 63103
140 S. Beacon St.
San Francisco, Calif. 94080
laboratory equipment, instruments, and apparatus

Bel-Arts Products
Pequannock, N. J. 07440
lab ware and plastic products

Biolab, Inc.
Box 222
Derry, N.H. 03038
lab ware and plastic products

Carolina Biological Supply Company
Burlington, N.C. 27215
biological specimens and supplies

Central Scientific Company (Cenco)
2600 S. Kostner Ave.
Chicago, Ill. 60623
(many branches)
supplies for chemistry, earth science, physics, and biology

Curtain Scientific Company
Box 1546
Houston, Texas 77001
supplies for chemistry and biochemistry

Dahl Company
P.O. Box 566
Berkeley, Calif. 94701
biological specimens and supplies

Fisher Scientific Company
(Stansi Educational Materials Div.)
1231 N. Honore St.
Chicago, Ill. 60622
supplies for chemistry, earth science, physics, and biology

GM Mfg and Instruments
2417 3rd Ave.
Bronx, N.Y. 10451
oceanographic and limnological supplies

Hach Chemical Company
Box 907
Ames, Iowa 50010
testing equipment and chemicals for aquatic biology

LaMotte Chemical Company
Chestertown, Md. 21620
testing equipment and chemicals for aquatic biology

LaPine Scientific Company
6001 S. Knox Ave.
Chicago, Ill. 60629
920 Parker St.
Berkeley, Calif. 94710
biological supplies and equipment

Matheson Scientific
1850 Greanleaf Ave.
Elk Grove, Ill. 60007
24800 Industrial Blvd.
Hayward, Calif. 94545
supplies for physical sciences

Millipore Corporation
Bedford, Mass. 01730
*supplies for environmental micro-
biology*

Nalge
Dept. 4117B
Rochester, N.Y. 14602
plastic lab ware

Scientific Products
1210 Leon Pl.
Evanston, Ill. 60201
scientific supplies and equipment

Sherman, H. B.
P.O. Box 683
Deland, Fla. 32720
folding live traps

Turtox
8200 S. Hoyne Ave.
Chicago, Ill. 60620
biological supplies and equipment

Van Waters & Rogers Scientific
P.O. Box 2062
Terminal Annex
Los Angeles, Calif. 90054
P.O. Box 23
High Bridge Station
Bronx, N.Y. 10452
(many branches)
scientific supplies and equipment

Ward's Natural Science Establish-
ment, Inc.
P.O. Box 1712
Rochester, N.Y. 14603
P.O. Box 1749
Monterey, Calif. 93940
biological supplies and equipment

Wildlife Supply Company (Wildco)
2200 S. Hamilton St.
Saginaw, Mich. 48602
limnological supplies

Yellow Springs Instrument Company
Yellow Springs, Ohio 45387
*chemical and physical instrumenta-
tion*

OTHER USEFUL RESOURCES

Aquatic Biology Abstracts, Information Retrieval Ltd., London.

Guide to Scientific Instruments, Science, American Association for the Advancement of Science, 1515 Massachusetts Ave. N.W., Washington, D.C. 20005 (issued yearly).

Laboratory Guide to Instruments, Equipment, and Chemicals, American Chemical Society, Washington, D.C. (issued yearly).

National Meeting on Water Quality Criteria (Publication No. 416), American Society for Testing and Materials Technique, Philadelphia, Pa., 1966.

Pollution Equipment News, c/o Richard Rinbach, Sr., 8550 Babcock Blvd., Pittsburgh, Pa. 15237 (current materials, equipment, and advances in pollution science).

Water Newsletter, Water Information Center, Port Washington, N.Y., 1959 to date.

Water Pollution Abstracts, Great Britain Water Pollution Research Board, Her Majesty's Stationery Office, London.

Water Publication of State Agencies by Gerald J. Giefer and David K. Todd, Water Information Center, Port Washington, N.Y.

Water Quality Control Digest, Scientific and Technical Information Center, Division of Urban Extension, Wayne State University, Detroit, Mich., 1969 to date.

Water Quality Criteria: Report to the Secretary of the Interior of U.S. National Technical Advisory Committee on Water Quality Criteria, Federal Water Pollution Control Administration, Superintendent of Documents, Washington, D.C.

Water Quality Criteria Data Book, U.S. Government Printing Office, Washington, D.C., Vol. 1–3 to date.

Water Resources Abstracts, American Water Resources Association, Urbana, Ill., 1968 to date.

Water Resources Newsletter, American Water Resources Association, Urbana, Ill.

Selected References

This bibliography is not meant to be exhaustive. It identifies works of a survey or introductory nature. Further specialization will be possible from references found in the sources listed below.

American Public Health Association, *et al. Standard Methods for the Examination of Water and Wastewater.* 13th ed.; Washington, D.C.: A.P.H.A., 1971. — The "bible" (basis for determinations to meet legal water quality standards); technical, but full of information.

Bailey, R. M., E. A. Lachner, C. C. Lindsey, C. R. Robins, P. M. Roedel, W. B. Scott, and L. P. Woods. *A List of Common and Scientific Names of Fishes from the United States and Canada* (Special Publication No. 6), American Fisheries Society, 1970. — Systematic arrangement of fishes of North America indexed by common and scientific names.

Bakker, Elna. *An Island Called California.* Berkeley: University of California Press, 1971. — Very readable account of community structure of major California habitats.

Barnes, R. D. *Invertebrate Zoology.* 2nd ed.; Philadelphia, Pa.: Saunders, 1968. — Good general reference on invertebrates.

Benton, A., and William Werner. *Field Biology and Ecology.* 2nd ed.; New York: McGraw-Hill, 1966. — Good general work on field biology.

Buckman, H. O., and N. C. Brady. *The Nature and Property of Soils.* 7th ed.; London: Macmillan, 1969. — Good general reference.

Clarke, G. L. *Elements of Ecology.* New York: Wiley, 1954 (rev. 1967). — General ecology with marine/aquatic bias.

Coker, R. E. *Streams, Lakes, Ponds.* New York: Harper & Row, 1954. — Excellent paperback; covers a lot of material with an easy style.

Cox, G. W. *Laboratory Manual of General Ecology.* Dubuque, Iowa: Wm. C. Brown, 1967.

Darnell, R. M. *Organism and Environment.* San Francisco, Calif.: Freeman, 1971. — Laboratory manual emphasizing quantitative methods.

DeBell, G. *The Environmental Handbook.* New York: Ballantine and Friends of the Earth, 1970. — Written for the first Earth Day; collection of interesting readings.

Dietrich, G. *General Oceanography*. New York: Wiley, 1963. – Good general reference on physical oceanography.

Edmondson, W. T., ed. *Freshwater Biology*. 2nd ed.; New York: Wiley, 1966. – The famous "Ward and Whipple" used since 1918 as a primary source of identification of freshwater organisms.

Environmental Protection Agency. *Methods for Chemical Analysis of Water and Wastes*. Washington, D.C.: U.S. Government Printing Office, 1971. – Technical, sophisticated manual for water analysis.

Fassett, N. C. *A Manual of Aquatic Plants*. Madison: University of Wisconsin Press, 1969. – Authoritative, illustrated handbook.

Hazen, W. E. *Readings in Population and Community Ecology*. 2nd ed.; Philadelphia, Pa.: Saunders, 1970. – Excellent background source for contemporary ecology.

Herald, E. S. *Living Fishes of the World*. Garden City, N.Y.: Doubleday, 1961. – Interesting survey, natural history notes, many color photos.

Hickman, C. P. *Biology of the Invertebrates*. St. Louis, Mo.: C. V. Mosby, 1967. – Comprehensive text on the subject.

Humason, G. L. *Animal Tissue Techniques*. San Francisco, Calif.: Freeman, 1962. – Reference for specimen preparation.

Hutchinson, G. E. *The Ecological Theater and the Evolutionary Play*. New Haven: Yale University Press, 1965 (rev. 1969). – Collection of provocative lectures by Hutchinson; includes description of niche.

Hutchinson, G. E. *The Enchanted Voyage and Other Studies*. New Haven: Yale University Press, 1962. – Contains Hutchinson's famous paper, "Homage to Santa Rosalia or Why there are so many kinds of animals," with other related papers.

Hutchinson, G. E. *A Treatise on Limnology*. Vol. I: *Geography, Physics, and Chemistry*. New York: Wiley, 1957.

Hutchinson, G. E. *A Treatise on Limnology*. Vol. II: *Introduction to Lake Biology and the Limnoplankton*. New York: Wiley, 1967. – Hutchinson's two volumes form one of the classics of limnology; thorough, authoritative, and well written.

Hynes, H. B. N. *The Ecology of Running Waters*. Canada: University of Toronto Press, 1970. – Compendium of stream biology.

Keeton, W. T. *Biological Science*. New York: Norton, 1967.—One of the best "freshman" biology books. Many discussions of up-to-date biological concepts.

Kershaw, K. A. *Quantitative and Dynamic Ecology*. London: Edward Arnold, 1964.—Readable explanation of research design.

Kormondy, E. J. *Concepts of Ecology*. Englewood Cliffs, N.J.: Prentice-Hall, 1969.—Readable summary of major ecological principles.

Lagler, K. F., J. E. Bardach, and R. R. Miller. *Ichthyology*. New York: Wiley, 1962.—Stiff, but complete textbook of ichthyology.

Leopold, A. *A Sand County Almanac*. New York: Oxford University Press, 1949.—A great naturalist's thoughts about biology and philosophy.

Leopold, L., and K. S. Davis. *Water*. New York: Life Science Library, 1966.—Readable account of the basic nature of water and its uses by man.

Lewis, T., and L. R. Taylor. *Introduction to Experimental Ecology*. New York: Academic Press, 1967.—Valuable series of well-executed experiments emphasizing insects.

MacArthur, R., and J. Connell. *The Biology of Populations*. New York: Wiley, 1967.—Good introduction to the study of population ecology.

More, J. A., ed. *Science for Society: A Bibliography*. 2nd ed.; Washington, D.C.: Commission on Science Education of the American Association for the Advancement of Science, 1971.—Extensive and informative list of references on contemporary biology.

Morholt, E., P. F. Brandwein, and A. Joseph. *A Sourcebook for the Biological Sciences*. 2nd ed.; Sacramento: California State Department of Education, 1967. In depth compilation of teaching resources.

Needham, J. G., and P. R. Needham. *A Guide to the Study of Freshwater Biology*. 5th ed.; San Francisco: Holden-Day, 1970.—Compact source of identification for most common aquatic organisms; includes a methods section.

Oakshott, G. B. *California's Changing Landscape: A Guide to the Geology of the State*. New York: McGraw-Hill, 1972.—Interesting account of the geology of a diverse state.

Odum, E. P. *Fundamentals of Ecology*. 3rd ed.; Philadelphia, Pa.: Saunders, 1971.—One of the classics of ecology; this new edition includes a section on applications and technology.

Oosting, H. S. *The Study of Plant Communities*. San Francisco: Freeman, 1956.—Handy, well-written reference for terrestrial studies.

Pennak, R. W. *Fresh-Water Invertebrates of the United States*. New York: Ronald Press, 1953.—Best general reference on the subject; includes life history and ecology, as well as identification.

Pimlott, D. H. "Wolf Predation and Ungulate Populations in Ecology and Behavior of the Wolf." *American Zoologist* (7) 2:172–381, 1967.

Rakoff, F. B. "Automatic Water Sampler Monitors Pollution." *Popular Science* (201) 2:112, 1972.

Reid, G. K. *Ecology of Inland Waters and Estuaries*. New York: Van Nostrand-Reinhold, 1961.—Small but complete text on freshwater and brackish environments.

Russell-Hunter, W. D. *Aquatic Productivity*. New York: Macmillan, 1970.—Basics of limnological productivity; clear discussions and illustrations.

Ruttner, F. *Fundamentals of Limnology* (trans. by D. G. Frey and F. E. J. Fry). Canada: University of Toronto Press, 1963.—Traditional classic in limnology; well written and authoritative.

Shepard, P., and D. McKinley. *The Subversive Science: Essays toward an Ecology of Man*. Boston: Houghton Mifflin, 1969.—Collection of provocative and unconventional essays on man and his ecology.

Simpson, E. H. "Measurement of Diversity," *Nature,* 163:688, 1949.

Smith, G. M. *The Fresh-Water Algae of the United States*. Rev. ed.; New York: McGraw-Hill, 1950.—Valuable reference volume.

Smith, R. L. *Ecology and Field Biology*. New York: Harper & Row, 1966.—Very complete and carefully done book; much more resourceful than the title would imply; recommended bibliography.

Smith, R. L. *The Ecology of Man: An Ecosystem Approach*. New York: Harper & Row, 1972.—Papers reflecting man's influence on the global ecosystem.

Sokal, R. R., and F. J. Rohlf. *Biometry*. San Francisco, Calif.: Freeman, 1969.—Probably the best introduction to statistical methods; designed so that a self-teaching approach is possible.

Strobbe, M. A. *Environmental Science Laboratory Manual*. St. Louis, Mo.: C. V. Mosby, 1972.—Technically oriented manual; includes calibration procedure for Bausch and Lomb's Spectronic 20.

Trautman, M. B. *The Fishes of Ohio*. Columbus: Ohio State University Press, 1957. — Excellent treatment of most freshwater fishes likely to be generally encountered.

Usinger, R. L. *Aquatic Insects of California*. Berkeley: University of California Press, 1956. — Authoritative, with chapters by specialists in each group; substantial and useful introduction.

Watt, Kenneth E. *Principles of Environmental Science*. New York: McGraw-Hill, 1973. — Application of basic ecological principles to a variety of environmental sciences; concepts are developed in a logical progression; a clearly written synthesis.

Welch, P. S. *Limnological Methods*. New York: McGraw-Hill, 1948. — Dated, but still widely used reference for physical methods in limnology.

Wynne-Edwards, V. C. *Animal Dispersion in Relation to Social Behavior*. New York: Hafner, 1962. — Controversial, but interesting approach to the theory of population regulation.

The Peterson Field Guide Series edited by Roger Tory Peterson and published by Houghton Mifflin Company of Boston is a series of comprehensive field guides covering plants and animals of North America.

A Field Guide to Animal Tracks, Olaus J. Murie, 1954.

A Field Guide to Reptiles and Amphibians of the United States and Canada East of the 100th Meridian, Roger Conant, 1958.

A Field Guide to Rocks and Minerals, Frederick H. Pough, 1953.

A Field Guide to the Birds, rev. ed., Roger Tory Peterson, 1947.

A Field Guide to the Butterflies, Alexander B. Klots, 1951.

A Field Guide to the Insects of America North of Mexico, Donald J. Borror and Richard E. White, 1970.

A Field Guide to the Mammals, 2nd ed., William H. Burt and Richard P. Grossenheider, 1964.

A Field Guide to the Western Reptiles and Amphibians, Robert C. Stebbins, 1966.

A Field Guide to Western Birds, rev. ed., Roger Tory Peterson, 1961.

The Pictured-Key Nature Series of Wm. C. Brown Company of Dubuque, Iowa, is a series of basic identification keys.

How to Know the Beetles, Harry E. Jaques, 1951.
How to Know the Butterflies, Paul R. Ehrlich, 1961.
How to Know the Economic Plants, Harry E. Jaques, 1958.
How to Know the Fall Flowers, Mabel J. Cuthbert, 1948.
How to Know the Freshwater Algae, 2nd ed., George W. Prescott, 1970.
How to Know the Freshwater Fishes, 2nd ed., Samuel Eddy, 1970.
How to Know the Grasses, 2nd ed., Richard W. Pohl, 1968.
How to Know the Immature Insects, Chu Hung-Fu, 1949.
How to Know the Insects, Harry E. Jaques, 1947.
How to Know the Land Birds, 2nd ed., Harry E. Jaques and Mabel J. Cuthbert, 1970.
How to Know the Mammals, 3rd ed., Ernest S. Booth, 1971.
How to Know the Mosses and Liverworts, Henry S. Conard, 1956.
How to Know the Protozoa, Theodore L. Jahn, 1949.
How to Know the Seaweeds, rev. ed., E. Yale Dawson, 1956.
How to Know the Spiders, 2nd ed., B. J. Kaston, 1972.
How to Know the Spring Flowers, Mabel J. Cuthbert, 1949.
How to Know the Trees, Harry E. Jaques, 1946; rev. ed., Howard A. Miller, 1972.
How to Know the Water Birds, Harry E. Jaques and Roy Ollivier, 1960.
How to Know the Weeds, Harry E. Jaques, 1959; rev. ed. Rober E. Wilkinson, 1972.
How to Know the Western Trees, Baerg, 1955.
Living Things—How to Know Them, Harry E. Jaques, 1946.
Plant Families—How to Know Them, Harry E. Jaques, 1948.

Index

Boldface numbers indicate pages where definition of entry appears; asterisks indicate illustrations. Subject index is followed by index of organisms.

Index of Organisms